THE MAESTRO
&
MARIANNE

A LOVE STORY

"A towering celebration of the victory
of love over time."

Robert J. duRosier

Trafford
PUBLISHING®

The Library of Congress has catalogued this edition as follows:
duRosier, Robert Maestro & Marianne

p. cm. ISBN Printed in the United States of America 10 987654321
Order this book online at www.trafford.com/08-0971
or email orders@trafford.com

Most Trafford titles are also available at major online book retailers.

ISBN: 978-1-4251-6298-6

*We at Trafford believe that it is the responsibility of us all, as both individuals
and corporations, to make choices that are environmentally and socially sound.
You, in turn, are supporting this responsible conduct each time you purchase a
Trafford book, or make use of our publishing services. To find out how you are
helping, please visit www.trafford.com/responsiblepublishing.html*

*Our mission is to efficiently provide the world's finest, most comprehensive
book publishing service, enabling every author to experience success.
To find out how to publish your book, your way, and have it available
worldwide, visit us online at www.trafford.com/10510*

www.trafford.com

North America & international
toll-free: 1 888 232 4444 (USA & Canada)
phone: 250 383 6864 ♦ fax: 250 383 6804
email: info@trafford.com

The United Kingdom & Europe
phone: +44 (0)1865 487 395 ♦ local rate: 0845 230 9601
facsimile: +44 (0)1865 481 507 ♦ email: info.uk@trafford.com

10 9 8 7 6 5 4 3 2

IN MEMORY OF MY FATHER, who is my soul's match.

And to my **MOTHER**, the twinkle in my eye.

For my little girl **JOSETTE**—you are <u>everything</u> to me.

With special thanks to Carol Vandenboss,
and Ethel Saint-Claire, my very own angels.

CONTENTS

INTRODUCTION 7

Part I The Seeker of the Grail 15

1 *Beginning* 16
2 *Struggle* 32
3 *Resolve* 40

Part II The Chooser of Roads 47

4 *Breakthrough* 48
5 *Healing* 59
6 *Opportunity* 67

Part III The Philosopher's Stone 79

7 *Destiny* 80
8 *Non-anticipation* 86
9 *Pain* 102
10 *Pleasure* 109
11 *The Magic Island* 126

Part IV The Elixir of Life 145

12 *Love* 146
13 *Alchemy* 156
14 *The Stage* 166

Part V The Quickening 181

15 *The Pacific* 182
16 *C'est la Vie* 191

EPILOGUE 210

INTRODUCTION

"And think not you can direct the course of love, for love if it finds you worthy, directs your course."

KAHLIL GIBRAN 'THE PROPHET'

June, 1962 – Vancouver, British Columbia

Oh, those eyes. They were the first and last things anyone ever remembered about him.

She wanted to kiss him the moment she first saw him. Her gold bracelet slid down her lightly freckled forearm to the top of her wrist as she reached for a cigarette and pulled it to her mouth. She inhaled, crossed her legs and refocused her attention on the entertainer performing in the Copper Room at Harrison Hot-Springs Resort. He looked up from the keys of the piano and stared right into her eyes, blue as a cloudless summer day. He was seducing her without trying as his eyes, brown as coffee and equally as jolting, expressed more desire in a glance than days of dialogue could. She wasn't sure if he was looking at her, or into her - penetrating, caressing, and wondering. The unspoken passion seduced her like a gathering storm, threatening to change the landscape of her future.

The audience watched Guy duRosier perform, but his eyes were fixed on one person. Marianne Nopson turned to her friend and asked, "Is he staring at me?"

"Are you kidding Marianne, he's been singing the entire song to you."

Guy sat in front of the black, grand piano surveying the crowd but singing directly to Marianne. "*Femme du ma frenesie, toi le sel de ma vie. Vos yeux font mon frisson de corp avec la prevision.*" Marianne wanted to ask her friend Sarah what he was saying but she wouldn't take her eyes off of Guy long enough to turn her head. Guy took a sip from the cosmopolitan that sat on top of the piano, shifted on the bench to address the crowd and pulled the microphone to his mouth. He spoke in a whisper, shyly, compared to the way he sang. *"Bienvenue dams et monsieurs*, this next number is from 'West Side Story,' *merci."* Finished, he stood to a round of applause, bowed and walked over to his drummer Jacques Cote, who had accompanied him at his Carnegie Hall Concert the previous fall.

"Take five, Jacques. I'm going to speak to someone."

"D'accord, Guy."

Marianne watched nervously as Guy turned away from his band and approached her table. She straightened in her chair and met Guy's eyes with an openness that allowed him to move closer.

"Bon soir, je m'appelle Guy duRosier."

Guy extended his hand to Marianne and she stood up to greet him. Marianne offered her hand and Guy held it to his mouth letting his lips softly brush over her fingers.

Marianne's cheeks began to glow while she felt her body temperature elevate.

"My name is Marianne, and this is my friend Sarah."

"Forgive me, but my English is not perfect," Guy apologized.

He spoke French, Creole, Italian, Spanish, and Portuguese fluently—and English well enough to make himself understood.

"No Guy, please don't apologize. Your accent is beautiful," said Marianne.

His very name was like velvet. It suggested class. It fit its owner in every respect. Guy duRosier was educated at St. Louis de Gonzague in Port au Prince, Haiti. It was there that the prodigy began performing professionally for the Issa Saieh Orchestra, Haiti's most famous. He had his first hit song, "Her Name is Michaelle," at the age of fourteen and the revenue from the record was timely as Guy's father, Andre duRosier, died that same year. Because of the repressive regime in Haiti, under the dictatorship of Francois 'Papa Doc' Duvalier, Guy left Haiti for Paris in 1960; he was in his early twenties. He settled in Paris and was a regular performer at the jazz club 'Mars', playing the saxophone, and was at the center of a growing intellectual and artistic Haitian community in Paris. While there, the famous French soprano Edith Piaf saw Guy perform and labeled him, "The living breath of Haiti." After a few years in Paris, Guy was offered an engagement in Vancouver, British Columbia. He welcomed the opportunity to travel and improve his English.

"Would you like to join us for dessert?" Marianne asked.

"*Non, chère* I have to finish up the third set in a few minutes – *merci beaucoup.* If you and your friend would like to come to my suite after the show for coffee, you are most welcome."

Guy stood, again taking Marianne's hand into his own and kissing it.

"*Enchantè de faire votre connaisance.*"

Marianne could hardly wait for a translation from her friend, and Sarah, expecting her impatience said, "He is enchanted to meet you." Marianne sighed, sat back down and smiled.

In the time it took for Guy to walk across the stage and sit down at the piano, Marianne had several questions run through her mind. How could she be falling in love with this man who was older, more sophisticated, and black? She was aware of the racial climate in the early sixties in America, having seen race riots and freedom marches on the news. She hated racism. Marianne had the inner strength to do what she wanted – even when it wasn't popular. This confidence shaped her personality. The question she didn't have a ready answer for: what would her father say if he saw her with Guy? She knew the answer but chased it out of her mind and turned her attention to Guy.

After the show, the general manager of the resort ate dinner and dessert with Guy and his band.

"Guy, I took the liberty of ordering some Haitian coffee for you and your band. I hope you will enjoy it."

"*Ah monsieur, c'est magnifique,*" Guy answered.

The owner stood to shake hands with the band, congratulated them on the show, then walked back through the kitchen to the lobby.

Guy's attention was divided, with one eye on his dessert and the other on Marianne.

"Will you excuse me Jacques? I am going to take some coffee with the young lady over there."

"Of course Guy, enjoy yourself."

Guy pulled his chair out, straightened his coat, and excused himself. Just a few steps away, he pivoted and returned to ask Jacques a question.

"Jacques, do I say *take* some coffee, or *have* some coffee?"

"I'm not certain Guy, but maybe your friend can give you some English lessons, *non?*"

Guy smiled at his precocious friend and turned toward Marianne's table.

He bowed slightly, and said, "Would you like to take some coffee with me?" Marianne stood quickly to go to Guy's suite and Sarah excused herself saying she could not come.

"No *chère*, I insist you both join me."

They walked along the stone path lined on each side by giant noble fir trees. The torch-lit path extended behind the main property to individual suites nestled just in front of a forest of pine trees.

"Isn't Vancouver beautiful?" Guy said.

"Yes it is. Sarah and I are from Seattle, Washington which is a two or three hour drive south from here."

Guy opened the door for the girls.

"This is my first time to the Pacific. I am from Haiti, and I was performing the last few years in Paris before I came here."

Guy went into the kitchen to make some coffee while Marianne and Sarah whispered instructions to each other.

"Marianne," Sarah whispered, "He is such a gentleman, and he obviously likes you. I trust him to be alone with you if you want me to leave."

Guy returned with coffee for the girls and joined them in the front room.

Marianne felt the way she always imagined herself. In his presence, she felt like a princess. Though her middle class, Norwegian background suggested otherwise, she felt most alive when she was dressed in a formal gown and adorned in jewelry. Guy brought out the best in her. She talked with him long into the evening after Sarah left. She was with Guy from Friday evening to Sunday except for the moments she returned to her room to change clothes and freshen up.

Guy and Marianne spent Sunday afternoon in each other's arms. Marianne propped herself up on the pillow to stare at Guy while he slept. She stared at him for hours, examining his face, memorizing it to console herself in his absence.

"How long have you been watching me sleep darling?" Guy asked.

"For a long time," she said. "You have such an interesting and handsome face."

Guy sensed a longing in her eyes and an intense desire to know where they were going with their feelings. He sat up to look into Marianne's eyes.

"My time with you has not, and will never take the shape of a summer affair. There is a difference between passion and love Marianne— this is greater than passion."

She curled up into Guy's arms, laid her cheek across his chest, and promised to come back to him every weekend.

By summer's end, Marianne had a secret that would no longer conceal itself. She stood in front of the mirror in her bedroom rubbing her hand slowly back and forth over her slightly bulging stomach. The skin felt soft but stretched and her naval was starting to protrude. She waited nearly four months to break the news to her mother and father, but she knew the time for truth had arrived. She was caught between dissipating youth and becoming a woman. She spent days wondering what her baby might look like, imagining a son with light brown skin and curly hair. A big smile came to her lips. She savored it knowing that in a few minutes when she finished saying those difficult words to her mother and father, true happiness might evade her for the rest of her life.

The veins popped out of Einar Nopson's forearm as he gripped the steering wheel tight enough to pull it out of the car's dash. Marianne knew that his silence was worse than rage. He seethed. For a moment she thought of getting out of the car in Blaine, Washington at the Canadian border and running until she dropped. She loved Guy, and she was afraid for him.

Her father made the sedan look tiny. He stretched his six-foot five-inch frame out as far as the seat would allow, and maintained his reticence the entire way to Harrison Hot Springs.

Einar Nopson went straight to the general manager to demand that he fire Guy immediately. Then he found Guy. Guy was made to understand that he would never see Marianne again. He was told in no uncertain terms that the price of his refusal to leave Marianne alone would be his life. The general manager arrived after Einar Nopson with a torn up copy of Guy's contract.

"Mr. duRosier, you and your band are terminated effective immediately. I suggest you return to Paris."

Marianne was held back from Guy by her father's forearm. But before they could slam the door in his face, Guy said, "Darling, this is love that has degenerated into passion at the hands of racists." He straightened, looked Einar Nopson in the eye, and asserted, "Racism has no scientific basis." His eyes narrowed underneath two furrowed brows, fixing a penetrating stare at Marianne's father, fighting for his woman with his eyes, with his disdain, rather than his fists. Guy finally looked away from Einar Nopson and turned his back on him just as the door slammed shut. He and Jacques returned to Paris the following day.

Marianne sat on a wooden bench beside the garden at the Bothell Home for Unwed Mothers. She shook her head at the irony of her situation, but the alternative was unthinkable. Her father gave her a choice. Put the child up for adoption or leave his house and never return. That was no choice. She became fierce. She grew all the way up that moment. Her suitcase couldn't have been filled faster, nor the door slammed behind her harder. The flowers in the garden softened her anger and reminded her of more poetic things—like her time with Guy. The memory of his face was all she had left. Her fists clenched into a ball. How could she have failed to get a photograph, or address from him? She wasn't even certain how to spell his last name. Marianne Nopson was alone. Alone.

March 14th, 1963 – Seattle, Washington

Two nurses walked side-by-side down the third-floor hallway of the University of Washington hospital. They were responding to a page from room number 156 occupied by a young red headed girl. As they rounded the corner and entered her room they could see in her eyes questions begging to be answered.

"My baby's father is black but he is so light."

"Pigmentation often shows up later in bi-racial babies," one nurse responded.

Two social workers from the Catholic Children's Services' Orphanage in Seattle arrived the following morning to counsel Marianne. One of them, a young woman just out of college, spoke first. "It can be very difficult to place bi-racial babies into permanent homes but we can assure you we'll find an interim care foster home for him." Marianne looked at both of the social workers and realized they weren't much older than she. But they lived in vastly different worlds. Marianne was forced to make an agonizing decision.

She picked up the pen then put it back down on the table. She shook her head back and forth whispering to herself, "No, no, no."

If only her older sister had not just had a stillborn child maybe she would have taken her baby until Marianne could get on her feet. Marianne picked up the pen one more time. She cried onto the adoption paperwork while the pen shook in her hand. She signed her name and asked, "Where will he be taken from here?"

"We'll take him downtown to Catholic Children's Services' Orphanage, Marianne," said the caseworker.

"We'll immediately begin attempting to place him in a home. But he will be taken care of until then, we assure you."

Marianne reached out to hug the little infant boy whom the nurses had given the name Pierre. But they would not let her touch her baby. The pain in her heart was more than she could take. Marianne went limp in her bed.

Walking seemed difficult. She was weak. Marianne leaned against her mother as they made their way down the hallway to the elevator and out the glass doors to exit the hospital. Tears covered her cheeks. Her eyes, nearly swollen shut and red bespoke an inner tragedy.

A continent away, sitting at the piano inside the Olympia Theater in Paris, France, Guy duRosier struggled with a pain in his stomach and unexplainable tears welling in his eyes. His fragile feelings were far too close to the surface, especially during a rehearsal; uncharacteristically he just could not concentrate. He discreetly wiped the wetness from the corner of his left eye, and managed in a broken voice to shout instructions to his orchestra, "One more time, from the top."

As Marianne passed through the swinging doors, she looked back as if her longing might change things. Had she been two floors up, she would have seen an infant boy given the name Pierre by the nurses, squirming restlessly in the arms of a state adoption caseworker—sensing a fate entirely out of his hands. He cried loudly, and Marianne cried with him.

Part I

THE SEEKER OF THE GRAIL

"The years of searching in the dark for a truth that one feels but cannot express, the intense desire and the alternations of confidence and misgiving, until one breaks through to clarity and understanding, are only known to him who has himself experienced them."

ALBERT EINSTEIN

1

BEGINNING

I CLUNG tightly to Ione Bannister's polyester pant leg, scratching her leg out of fear. Too many children had come and gone from the Bannister household to trust that I wasn't the next child to leave, so I measured the unfamiliar faces of the man and woman at the front door. They were waiting to take me to a Seattle Totems hockey game. The man's face scared me, but the woman's was kinder. Still, I hid behind the blue polyester pants, digging my fingernails in to get a fist full of fabric, determined not to let go, scared of staying yet even more terrified of leaving with these strangers. I was not old enough to articulate my feelings coherently so I wailed and wailed, expressing myself the only way that I could. This was how it happened, how the other little kids went away and never returned. It seemed innocent, but as a foster child the strange faces at the front door represented not innocence but—to me—danger.

I felt my fingertips being pried from their stranglehold on the polyester and being lifted off the floor by the man whose face I did not like. I screamed as he pivoted to walk away, my vision blurred by tears, making it difficult to focus on Ivo and Ione Bannister. It was like looking through a window with rain pouring down the glass: I saw Ivo standing beside Ione in his coveralls with the bill of his hat flipped up. I was certain I'd never see them again. I remembered Katie leaving the same way as a baby. She never came back. I wondered where she went, and why she had to go there. I could not imagine an answer, and I didn't know how to ask anyone else: I was too little to verbalize my questions, but not too little to be terrified.

The ice arena contained the largest gathering of people I had ever seen.

Everywhere I looked, faces screamed toward the ice. I just felt cold and continued sobbing into the woman's shoulder, soaking her coat. By the second period we got up to leave. I peered out the car window until the hum of the engine and the rolling motion of the car put me to sleep. When I woke, I was relieved to see that we were back at the Bannister's house, parked in the front. Perched securely on the man's shoulder, I looked up at the familiar light above the front door; I was almost close enough to touch the bugs whizzing around the light.

Back inside the house, I headed to the basement bedroom and changed into my pajamas. I timed my leap into bed while simultaneously switching off the light, leaving the room pitch black. I jumped inside my sleeping bag, using it like a cocoon rather than getting underneath the bed covers. I pulled the sleeping bag up over my head to shut out any of the monsters I knew were there but which would disappear the moment I turned on the lights.

That night was like others, in that once I was wrapped up tightly in my own little cocoon, isolated, the tears came. Sometimes falling hotly down my cheeks, then rolling right into my ears, and sometimes rolling straight down and splashing on my collarbone, almost tickling, they reminded me that I was lost. Even as a three-year-old I wondered, "Where are my people. Where do I belong?"

"Bobby Jo," Ione Bannister hollered, "Molly's at the front door waiting for you." I jumped up from in front of the television and ran to my dresser. Ione followed me and picked out some clothes. She tucked in my shirt and quickly tied my shoes, then pointed me toward the front door.

"Be a good boy," she said, as she licked her thumb, then used it to wipe away the remains of my breakfast from my chin.

"I will, mommy," I obeyed.

Molly Holloway's long brown hair fell down past her shoulders, resting on her beige raincoat. A brown scarf protected her petite neck from the dense fall air. I tilted my head back as far as possible to see her face.

"Hi Molly," I smiled.

She bent all the way down, placing her open palms on my cheeks, and said, "Hi Bobby. Would you like to go for a walk with me?" I nodded my head up and down while widely grinning. My intuition assured me that Molly Holloway, my adoption caseworker, was my ally, and I had my usual set of questions ready to ask her.

Holly trees and mature evergreens lined both sides of Twenty-sixth Avenue South, a middle class, Seattle neighborhood just a few miles from the Boeing aerospace company. Molly held my hand gently in hers as we walked down the street, my two or three steps trying to keep pace with each one of hers.

I looked up and asked, "Molly, how come Billy's gone?" Before she could answer, I added, "Where did he go? Did he go where Katie went?" Billy shared a crib with me until I was big enough for a twin bed, but when he was still in the crib, he banged his head against the crib posts. It was rhythmic, as if he couldn't help it-– bang, bang, bang-–pause— bang, bang, bang.

"Billy's sick honey, so we are helping him as much as we can, and looking for a family for him."

"Am I going away too Molly?"

Her eyes watered up as she stopped in mid-step and squatted down to look directly into my questioning eyes.

"Bobby dear, I am doing my very best to find a permanent home for you. Until then, you will be staying here with the Bannister's."

"Okay Molly."

The relief of her gentle eyes fixed squarely on mine sustained me through my disappointment. What Molly Holloway knew but couldn't convey to me was frightening. No white family wanted a mixed race— half-black and half-white child-and no black family did either. I was too young to understand racism and the effect it had on my life, but my epidermis had placed me in this holding station called foster care. *I must have had another name besides Bobby Bannister.* I knew I was only using their name-–it wasn't my own. Before she knocked on the front door, I tugged on Molly's coat and said, "I always act right, Molly."

"I know you do, honey. You keep it up for me, okay?"

I nodded my head. She hugged me, opened the door and promised to visit me again soon.

I counted four candles on the birthday cake sitting in the middle of the long dining table occupied at one end by Ivo Bannister, and flanked by Floyd, Louise, Linda, Barbara, Kathy and another foster child, Karen. Ione stood over Ivo's left shoulder with a camera and directed, "Blow out your birthday candles, Bobby Jo." I looked at all the faces smiling back at me and grinned widely; however, my happiness had nothing to do with my birthday. Billy and Katie never made it to four candles. They had to go someplace else, but I didn't. My happiness arrived in small victories, in longevity with one family and in a precarious sense of belonging. These victories, measured in time, sustained me.

The dim lights in the classroom cast shadows against the wall where Sister Celeste stood in her black robe and white habit--the uniform of the Franciscan Order. We sat in five rows, evenly spaced. Our feet were on the floor and our hands were folded, ready for prayer. My uniform consisted of salt-and-pepper slacks and a crisp white shirt under a brown sweater. The girls wore plaid skirts well below their knees.

"Now children, we will have quiet during this film," said Sister Celeste as she started the projector. Her white habit fit snugly around her head and ears, leaving only her forehead, eyes, nose and mouth visible. While the projector whirred and rattled to a start, she paced each of the five rows tapping a ruler firmly into her open palm as a reminder to keep our mouths closed. The title of the film appeared against the large screen that was pulled down in front of the chalkboard: "The Advent of the Steam Engine." The steam engine plowed through rock quickly while opposite the engine, John Henry, a massive, muscled black man, used a pickaxe on the rock. They were moving side-by-side when, at last, the steam engine won the race.

At recess, one of the boys pushed me and smirked, "Hey, look at John Henry." Several of my classmates laughed. I nudged him back with my elbow as I tried to reclaim my spot in line. He spit on me, covering the side of my face. Pride told me to hit the boy, but my fear told me I would be gone, cast off to wherever Billy and Katie and the other kids went. I feared that knock on the door in the middle of the day announcing an adoption caseworker handling paperwork in one hand and clutching a briefcase in the other. I feared Molly having to take me away. Still, I punched the kid right in the mouth, cutting both his lip and my knuckles.

The Principal's office of a Catholic school was no place for a first grade student to be, even if it meant a chance of exoneration. Sister Imelda looked one hundred years old and was even more imposing than my teacher, Sister Celeste. Sister Imelda made her way out of her office carrying a large paddle perforated on the end to improve the speed at which a swat could be administered. She strolled calmly past the secretary and stood between Richard Danak and me. She began pacing, showing off the equalizer in her right hand. Richard sat quietly with a smirk on his face as though this sort of thing was common, while I did my best to hide my tears. I cried not from fear, but from the shock of the violence that I encountered.

"Dry up those alligator tears right now Bobby Bannister," Sister Imelda said stoically.

"Yes Sister."

Her face then tensed after looking at Richard Danak, "You come with me young man." I heard the paddling along with Richard's cries twenty feet away as I walked back to my classroom.

That night, Ivo Bannister told me never to start a fight but to always finish one. I was happy to have him on my side, but something insidious gnawed at me—the ignorance of my own color. My dad's face was white, his nose straight, his hair, straight and black. All of the other faces in the house were like his and my mom's. This film about the steam engine versus John Henry, and the ensuing racist remark at recess, halted my innocence in its tracks. I was forced to make distinctions based on color. I already knew I was different. My innocence was lost in the manipulation of differences. People were capable of using differences to hurt me, leaving me vulnerable to ridicule. I never anticipated that. I was busy pleasing my foster family so that I could stay in it. Now I had to shepherd my pride to ensure that ridicule and racism couldn't defeat me. At the age of six, I had become a warrior inside.

I had no alternative. I succeeded because I had to-because I found myself in situations that demanded my all. I found dignity in self-reliance, and my courage was not the absence of fear, but rather the judgment that something else was more important than fear. I paid a price for this guardianship of myself, though. I became emotionally unavailable, even unflappable. I was prepared for the worst before it could happen to me. This left me so still inside that I was completely free to respond immediately and in all directions.

Being made to feel different defined for me a new truth, "*I must know my biological Mother and Father.*" Not maybe. Not kind of. I had to know them.

I timidly approached Ivo Bannister in the garage. "Dad, can you tell me anything about my mother and father?" He looked shocked to hear me ask the question that he had hoped would never come. I avoided eye contact with him and shuffled from side to side with my hands in my pockets, waiting patiently for his response. He carefully adjusted his weight off of the front quarter panel of the 1969 Ford Fairmont he was working on and put his crescent wrench into the front pocket of his grease-laden coveralls.

"Well Bobby Jo, your adoption was closed. That means we were not allowed any information about your mother or father. The court has that information sealed and will not release it until you turn twenty-one."

Twenty-one was a lifetime away for me. I felt like a stranger in the house; like I was spending the night at a friends house but I was on a perpetual sleep over. A hot tear ran down my cheek. My frustration, anger, and helplessness showed. Ivo Bannister saw this and remarked, "We think we know that your Mother was very young when she had you…and that your Father was a Tahitian sailor."

The six feet between Ivo and me may as well have been the Pacific Ocean. He stood on one side, and I stood on the other. Just then a hug may have saved my life, but we had the Pacific Ocean between us. I turned and walked up to my bedroom.

I didn't eat dinner that night. Instead, I lay awake in bed pleading with God to give me my mother and father back.

"I'll be a good boy God if you just let me see my mommy once."

That prayer became a habitual bedtime request. Night after night, year after year, I was left with an illusion—the image of a sailor and a young girl.

The black rotary telephone reached its third ring before I started to incorporate the loud ringing into my dream. I got out of bed and scampered down the hallway in my Batman pajamas, certain that my biological mother was on the other end of the telephone. By the fifth ring I was startled out of my dream when Ione Bannister called, "Bobby, Sister Celeste is on the phone. She's calling to make sure you'll be on time to serve today's eight a. m. Mass."

I preferred my dream, complete with my biological mother talking to me on the phone, telling me she was coming for me soon. The interruption snapped me reluctantly back to reality.

"Okay, Mom," I answered. "I'm getting up right now."

By 7:50 a.m. I was in the sacristy behind the church altar at Our Lady of Lourdes. The altar boys' uniforms hung crisply, separated by class grades: first grade through eighth grade. I reached into the closet to pull out my red robe and white lace shirt.

"Well top o' the mornin' to ya there Bobby," Father Sean Heenihan chirped in his thick Irish accent.

"Good morning Father Heenihan," I answered while wiping the sleep from my eyes with the corner of my sleeve. I watched Father Heenihan consecrate the Eucharist, and then shine the chalices' to perfection. He wore a majestic purple robe over his black-on-black civilian clothes.

If I allowed my eyes to blur, the first long row of pews in front of the altar looked to be filled by a colony of penguins. I amused myself this way every Sunday, but I did not allow the ten Franciscan nuns, dressed in black and white, to see me break a smile. Each of them had one eye on me at all times, searching for the slightest indiscretion. *'Keep your shoulders back young man; get that chin up; fold your hands this way not that.'*

The perfect altar boy's reward was an almost imperceptible gesture from the Principal, Sister Imelda, delivered at the end of mass as the priest and two altar boys met in front of the altar to genuflect. An ever so slight bow of the forehead down and back up meant I was golden. I watched for it every Sunday and so did Ivo and Ione Bannister, seated perpendicular to the nuns in the front row. Kids from the public school at the other end of the block walked by after church and held hands, kissed, cursed, fought, and threw rocks. I saw it all. Everything they were doing would have gotten me expelled from my school. I attended Our Lady of Lourdes Catholic grade school and was the youngest of five other Bannister children in the school. I was an honors student and excelled in sports not because of some insatiable academic or athletic appetite but because I knew that if I was a good boy and got good grades, the Bannisters would have a tough decision if it came to letting me go. After mass, I sprinted up the driveway and bolted through the door, changed out of my shirt and tie as quickly as possible, and gathered my baseball gear into a gym bag.

Rain sprinkled down on the windshield of the 1957 Chevy, tempering my enthusiasm for my first all-stars baseball practice for the area eleven and twelve-year-olds.

"Tell me when the light changes young man," Ivo Bannister ordered as he opened the driver's side door to spit out a stream of brown liquid generated from his Copenhagen chewing tobacco. The scent of tobacco indicated a rare good mood settling in.

"The light is green now Dad," I answered.

I put my Rawlings, Reggie Jackson autographed glove on my left hand, brought it up to my nose, and smelled the combination of leather and glove oil with a hint of Copenhagen chewing tobacco from across the bench front seat of the car.

"Those twelve-year-olds might be a year older than you Bobby Jo, but you're just as big as they are and every bit as good, young man. You go show 'em who's boss just like Floyd did when he was your age." My older brother, Floyd, was a legend in the area baseball community. He had dominated at every level and had just made the collegiate All-American first team. He was being projected as the number one draft pick in the nation. On any baseball diamond I stepped onto, I had enormous shoes to fill because every coach knew me from my last name. In the dugout that morning, I heard whispers from various guys, "That's Floyd Bannister's brother. He's not as good as his brother though." I heard this so often that it served to motivate me, but when I did exceptionally well, it was expected, and when I didn't it was noteworthy. I wished it could have been the other way around.

Still, I loved the game and it was as close a bond with my dad as I had. Weekdays at four in the afternoon, I sat on the porch steps in front of the house, waiting for Ivo Bannister to get home from work. Both of our gloves rested in my hands, and like a sentry I waited for his car to pull up. He'd oblige me and toss the ball around for about thirty minutes before he ever stepped foot into the house. I feared him every moment, except the moments when we played catch, but the beauty of our backyard game of 'catch' was that it humanized him in my eyes, because even though we seldom spoke, there was an unspoken language in the pop of the leather and the whiz of the baseball. "Hit me in the chest Bobby Jo, put 'er right there young man." That was as close as he got to saying, "I love you Bobby Jo, and don't worry about a thing. We're going to adopt you soon and you'll always be a part of the family." That's how I translated it. I imagined the kind of love that I needed, the kind of words I needed to hear.

The Fourth of July was another special day because he came close to bonding with me then too. He made homemade ice cream every Fourth and chose me over all seven children to turn the crank that would shave the ice: my special little duty. I'd get to sit beside him too.

Very seldom were we ever in close proximity. That's not to say it was his fault. I didn't usually allow it, or put myself in that position with him or my mom. By not being affectionate, I was protecting my emotions from the real prospect of leaving the family. It always came down to that for me. It shaped my interpersonal relationships and dictated the dynamics for me in both one-on- one, and group, or family interactions. In a group setting, I was an observer. I looked at Floyd, Linda, Barbara, Louise, Kathy, and Karen, and I saw a likeness in their faces. Some looked just like Mom, and others favored Dad. Then I saw my face, my hair, an afro, very curly, and my olive skin, where theirs was very white. I saw my wide nose and nostrils, theirs, skinny and straight, and my completely different body type. I was tall and lean. They tended to be thicker, heavier and shorter. With every moment, I was reminded that I was different. They never made me feel like an outsider. They didn't have to. I simply was.

At the end of the day, in the privacy of my bed, I dreamed, hoped, and protected myself with my thoughts and prayers. Then I replenished my tank for the challenge that would meet me with every sunrise. The warrior was great. I was worthy. This was my only choice: pride that bordered on arrogance, or complete self-destruction based on fear.

When I turned twelve years old, something began to change. Kids no longer were coming and going at the rate they were before, leaving three foster children—Tim Johnson, who was a year older than I, Karen, two years younger, and me.

One evening, Tim Johnson came downstairs to my bedroom to get me to sneak upstairs with him and snatch some cookies. The thought seemed innocent but the horror of getting caught by Ivo Bannister, especially after bedtime, was real. I went all the way to the top of the stairs with Tim, each stair creaking and cracking until he got to the landing.

"Come on Bobby, we'll get some cookies," he whispered.

"No, I'm not going. I'm going back downstairs."

He whispered something about me being a sissy. As I lay awake in bed I heard the frightening heavy footsteps of my father pace quickly across the living room floor into the kitchen. Then I heard the even more frightening voice disciplining Tim Johnson.

"How old are you young man?" Ivo Bannister barked.

"Thirteen, sir."

I heard it all the way downstairs-–the round metal clip of the leather strap he used for beatings, sliding off the hanging rod just to the left of the back porch door. The metal-on-metal sound paled in comparison to the sound that strap made when Ivo Bannister was getting ready to use it. Two strips of twelve-inch-long hard leather straps a quarter of an inch thick hung down from the metal clip. He bowed them out as far as they would go before popping them back together to make a terrifying, snapping sound. I never knew which was worse-the actual beating, or the pleasure Ivo Bannister took in making that popping sound with the belt just before he used it. It was the precursor to pain, and the masochistic reminder of absolute power in the Bannister home. The crispness of the sound conjured up red welts in my mind.

"Well, then thirteen it is."

Tim's cries started sooner than I expected, around the third whipping. He had ten to go so I grabbed my pillow and put it over my ears, thinking about anything else besides what I knew was happening upstairs. It wasn't long before there were just two foster kids living in the Bannister home, Karen and me. Tim was gone.

The next time I saw Molly Holloway, I had no time for small talk. If a child could leave the house I lived in over chocolate chip cookies, then the eggshells that I walked on just became seriously fragile. Everything about me had changed except for my question for Molly that used to come every other month, but now just semi-annually. My growth spurt left my joints sore, but allowed me to look Molly directly in the eye.

"Goodness Bobby, you have really grown," she remarked, surprised that I was as tall as she.

"Molly, when are the Bannisters going to adopt me?" I asked, more impatiently than ever before. The question, delivered like an adult, deserved an adult answer. Molly Holloway spoke to me as an adult for the first time in my life, knowing the moment had arrived for the brutal truth. This time her answer was different and it terrified me, but she risked my fear because she knew I deserved to know.

"Bobby, listen carefully and try to understand me. Don't be scared because everything will be okay." I braced myself like a boxer unable to fend off a body blow, certain that the wind would be knocked out of me.

"There are no families that are willing to take a bi-racial child. I have been trying to place you into a permanent home for a long time now."

I feigned ambivalence, expertly avoiding eye contact with my favorite person until I could control my tears by biting down hard on my cheeks with my teeth.

"Bobby, are you okay?"

"Yes, Molly," I lied.

I hung my head and watched angrily as tears dropped down and splashed the toes of my Keds All Star's sneakers, betraying me. I had cried more than any boy should have to and I didn't mind if privacy concealed it, but I knew Molly could see.

"It's okay. Look at me honey," Molly said as she put the palms of her hands on my cheeks and kissed my forehead. I steeled myself with determination and looked her in the eyes, silently conveying my inner strength to her. My strength came from deep within, and I needed Molly to see it.

That fall, early morning windswept rains regularly hammered the windowpane above my bed. The rhythm was hypnotizing, percussive splattering that left me teetering peacefully between lucidity and the clarity of morning dreams. I would stay in that state until the scent of freshly-baked banana bread circled my warm covers like bait on a hook.

"Have a good day at work, and I'll see you around noon," Ione Bannister said to her husband as he shut his charcoal-grey lunch pail and snapped the silver handle latch securing it shut. That popping sound acted as my alarm clock signaling both Ivo Bannister's departure for work and breakfast for me. I waddled into the kitchen wiping sleep from my eyes and surveyed an array of baked goods on the countertop. My breakfast waited for me next to the stove where I saw my usual bowl full of bananas, floating like buoys in cold milk. I positioned myself at the table across from Ione and dug into my breakfast while watching 'Tom and Jerry' chase each other around the television set; they were a regular feature during *J.P. Patches*, a local variety hour program for kids. If I hurried, I'd catch the first few minutes of 'George of the Jungle,' and still get my school uniform on in time to leave the house at 7:30. At the commercial break, I put on my salt-and-pepper slacks and buttoned my white shirt but was interrupted by Ione Bannister, "Bobby Jo, you won't be going to school today. We have to go into the city and talk to some people. Molly will be there and your dad will be meeting us there too." She told me to put on my nice clothes.

I ripped off my school uniform and reached into the closet to find my suit; the sleeves and pant legs were too long, but they were the best hand-me-downs I had from Floyd. I tried to recall one occasion in my life when Ivo Bannister took time off of work...and came up blank. Like a well-oiled machine, he clocked in and punched out at the same time everyday, and most weekends too. The strangeness of this morning exhilarated and frightened me.

I wasn't used to going into the city. We never drove there, especially my mom and me alone.

We arrived at a tall building and proceeded inside. The elevator took us up higher than I had ever been in a building, and the speed of ascent was dizzying. When we stepped out, I saw Molly in the lobby talking with some people in business suits; important people. Ivo Bannister waited uncomfortably a distance away. He wore a pair of slacks and a dress shirt, foregoing his Osh-Kosh coveralls splattered with metal shavings from work as a machinist at Boeing. Seeing him out of his coveralls was as strange a sight as if I had seen a kangaroo in that lobby.

I followed Molly into a room that suggested business. A recently shined, majestic, cherry wooden table dominated the room. Molly sat beside me and held my hand. Her hazel eyes were a perpetual shock, leaving the rest of her face less important. I was either lost in the kindness of her eyes, or looked away from her entirely. She smiled and said, "Today is the day Bobby. The Bannisters will legally adopt you if you agree to it. If you are happy then everything will work out. Don't be afraid of these stuffy- looking people, they're just going to ask you some questions, so answer them honestly okay?"

"Okay. Will you sit beside me the whole time please?"

"Of course I will dear."

The questions were simple, but the simple truth was all that would be necessary that day. They asked me the same questions that Molly had asked for twelve years. 'Are you happy? Are you being treated well?'

I answered "yes" to everything. I was willing to be adopted. Paperwork requiring our signatures flooded the top of the shiny cherry wooden table. I signed over and over again, 'Robert Joseph Bannister,' just below the signatures of Ivo and Ione. *'Maybe now,'* I reasoned, *'I could call them Mom and Dad and feel confident about it.'* It took fifteen minutes. When I finished, Molly informed me that I was officially adopted into the Bannister's family. I was theirs and they were mine. Nothing changed that moment, and everything changed that moment. The precarious nature of my relationship with the Bannister family had shaped me into a careful, measured young boy. I hoped that our signatures, along with Molly's assurances, meant that I could spend my first day in twelve years of life, worry free. I gave Molly a hug goodbye, and she hugged me differently than ever before, like holding onto something that you don't ever want to let go. Something of great value passed between us that morning. She gave me a piece of her soul and said goodbye to me inside of that embrace. I stepped back, aware of our lack of privacy, but stared lovingly at her, determined to burn her image into my heart. She shook Ivo Bannister's hand and hugged Ione, then pressed the down button on the elevator's control panel. She walked back over to me and whispered in my ear, "I love you, Bobby."

"Me too, Molly."

The loud 'ding' signaled the elevator's arrival and my angel turned away from me and proceeded behind two steel doors that closed too rapidly. I wondered if I'd ever see my Molly again. Pain came attached to my pleasure like an unwanted companion.

I held my mom's hand in the lobby and looked up at her with a shy grin. She smiled back at me.

I took that day off from school and my mom stopped by McDonald's and bought me lunch. That was a rare occasion. And I recognized it as a special celebratory thing just between her and me. Sometimes when I was really sick, she would take me to McDonald's for a milkshake to make my throat feel better. These were our times, just like throwing the ball was my dad's time with me. She was always gentle with me, but I'm sure she sensed my wall come up often. However, she was more talkative with me than my dad. She always told me that I was a leader; I was special. "Hold yourself to a high standard," she would say. And she came to my baseball games and rooted louder than anybody else for me. She made the family tick. She was a housekeeper before that term was used. She simply was home all the time, running the family. She was always there. At times that irritated me because I was getting older and wanted to have friends over to goof around, but that would have only led to trouble anyway. It was a real blessing to have her home. It kept me in line.

I was finally able to let go of much of the insecurity I had carried. I didn't have the paralyzing fear of losing my family at any given moment.

Still, I carried the habit from infancy and it would not be easy to trust in anything. But I was happier than ever. Now the only issues I had to be concered with were residual. Things like racism. That was a piece of cake compared to wondering about the very basic security inside of a family. My relief was obvious. I was so much more comfortable. I was opening up more at dinner and sharing feelings about my day. I would even occasionally ask for help, or advice. Those were things I had never done. If I had a problem at school, and there were several, I had always kept it to myself.

Sometimes kids at school would call me 'nigger'. Often times they were the bigger kids one or two grades up from mine, and it usually happened at recess or in the school halls. When it did happen, I would always, always look them in the eye until they looked away. They may have been too big to fight, but I never let them win the battle of spirit. Not once. I defeated them every time with my gaze and with my pride. One of the boys, an eighth grader, got so angry when he couldn't rattle me, that he punched me in the neck and shoulder. I was in the sixth grade and he was one of the biggest boys in the school. Because I was big for my age, sometimes the eighth graders would invite me to play kick ball at recess with them. But Tim Hubert was not interested in that. He yelled from about thirty feet, "Let that little nigger play with his own class." So I walked right past him never taking my eyes off of him. Our class played the same game at the other end of the field and when the eighth graders' ball came rolling into our area, I picked it up and held it. The bully came over for the ball, but instead, I kicked that rubber ball as far as was possible, down the street and it rolled and rolled about a block and a half. He came over and hit me so hard, that I couldn't lift my arm over my head for about three days. It was worth it. He tested my spirit. My will. He and everyone else would lose that challenge. What they didn't realize was that they were dealing with a warrior. I had years of preparation and I was already as scared as any kid could ever be. So these things were nothing to me.

Many of the Bannister children were growing older and leaving the house. Things were different without all of the commotion in the house. The number of kids had gone from seven to four. Louise, Linda, and Floyd had moved on. Louise and Linda had married and Floyd was the first Bannister child to attend college. I especially missed him because we were the only boys. I could look forward to playing whatever sport was in season after school with Floyd. But he was eight years older than I and had an entirely different peer group. So our closeness was limited to his teaching me to be a good baseball player. He never took it easy on me. Sometimes that frustrated me because I wanted to win and he never let me. But when I got around kids my own age, I usually dominated them because of my preparation with my older brother.

It was fun to have sisters too. They took care of me, protected me, and—without knowing they were doing so—taught me how to treat women. I saw what hurt them, what made them happy, how emotional they could be, and how to get along with them. My older sisters were more mothering than anything else towards me, especially Linda. They were kind to me. Barbara, Kathy, Karen and I were left in the house. I was getting older and starting to really grow fast, already six feet tall by the eighth grade. I was beginning to recognize some of my strengths in terms of academics. I was easily literate and lyrical. Poems or stories were simple for me to write. I always got A's in English. These talents weren't nurtured in the home however. Ivo Bannister was the opposite. His was a mechanic's mind, an engineer's demeanor. He'd take apart an engine and have it back together in no time. I was often called on to help him, but it completely bored me. I never even knew which way to turn a screw. My mind worked differently, so I kept my love of literature and the arts to myself.

One of my first big accomplishments came in the eighth grade. The Catholic Dioceses of Seattle were holding a spelling bee. The winner received a full scholarship to any of the Catholic High Schools in the greater Seattle area. I qualified by winning the contest at my school, then I competed against the school champions from all of the Catholic schools in Seattle. I finished second in the city and received a partial scholarship to go to Kennedy High School. I was so proud. Words came easily to me. I collected them like some kids collected baseball cards but near the end of the school year, I had to learn a hard lesson from the Franciscan Nuns about discipline. My brother and idol had come home for the weekend from Arizona State. I hadn't seen him in months and I was just thrilled to see him. He brought me tee shirts with the university seal and I thought I was just the coolest kid around. I was so proud of my brother. On Sunday, he attended mass with my family and I was serving the mass as an altar boy. He sat in the front row just a few feet from the altar. I kept looking at him and every time our eyes met, he tried to make me laugh by making funny faces at me. I laughed so hard that I almost choked. After mass, Sister Imelda took me firmly by the arm and led me from the sacristy to an empty stairwell. "Bobby Bannister, if you cannot conduct yourself in a dignified manner during mass, then you are no longer a part of the honor society and your scholarship is hereby taken away." As simple as that, it was given to Mark O'Brien. I couldn't believe it. My mom protested mildly to no avail. I was off of the altar boy roster as well for one month. I could live with that—I actually liked the time off. But the punishment had been dealt and I didn't think it fit the crime. Franciscan justice came swiftly and totally. Nonetheless, I learned not to cross the Franciscans. My fear was that I wouldn't be able to attend Kennedy High School like all of my brothers and sisters before me had. I dreamed of playing varsity baseball for Coach Joe Faccone, just like Floyd had. I intended to star there then go to Arizona State just like him. But my Mom reassured me that I would still be able to attend. That was a relief. Going to a public high school would have been like throwing me to the wolves. I was sheltered by my scholastic environment, naïve in many ways. So scholarship or no, four more years of Catholic school awaited me.

2

STRUGGLE

I's not until we are forced to face the conflict between our desires and reality that life really acquires meaning. Everybody faces adversity in some way. We all have our stories. It's the way that we face our dilemmas and move through life that shapes our character. That is the truest way to measure our lives. I learned that pain and suffering were necessary if there was to be joy, because joy is nothing but sorrow unmasked. And the deeper that sorrow cuts into your being, the more joy you can contain. How else can it be? I let myself feel the pain of my life. I knew that without my biological mother or father I was handicapped in several ways, but I also looked for the joy that my life held. I embraced the differences. Families seemed to take me in as one of their own all of the time. My friends were like extended family. I had a network of friends that were incredible.

It is difficult to take in every detail of a landscape all at once. It's impossible to know it in a single view. We look near, then far. Left, then right—so that our overall view is never whole but a composite of images for us to disseminate. The same is true in regard to one's life experiences. My teenage years were like everybody else's, at times exhilarating, and at times clumsy, even daunting.

My love for books and writing kept me focused academically, while my passion for baseball kept me preoccupied so much that trouble never found me. Teenagers position for an identity to single themselves out. It's that, or get lost in a sea of faces. It can't be underestimated how important baseball was to my sense of self worth. It was helpful too that I was the fifth Bannister child to come through John F. Kennedy High School. The administration may not have seen a likeness in me physically with all of the other Bannisters, but they knew my last name. That made the transition from a class of 16 to over 400 incoming freshman more tolerable.

At orientation I sized myself up with the crowd. I was no longer going to be the biggest, tallest or fastest kid. But there were only a handful of guys my size. There were very few minorities. I noticed three or four African American kids, more Asians, and only a few Hispanics. I felt different from all of them. But I knew I was a minority. And I found comfort in diversity. I gravitated towards it. Still, it is a very strange feeling to be bi-racial, especially black and white, because you aren't fully accepted by either group. You are a fringe player. You are half. I knew it. I had one foot in the door and the other foot out. And the most interesting thing about it is this: if you try too hard to get both feet in, they know you're trying too hard and you're not accepted. Conversely, if you don't make any effort to choose sides, you are labeled a snob, uppity, or high yellow. To experience racism from both blacks and whites is something else. It's tough to describe really. Hence, the infamous quote, "Tragic mulatto." But there are advantages inherent in diversity. I was unique, exotic. And I never had problems finding friends. People came to me. I heard it all. The questions covered just about every ethnicity. "Are you Brazilian? Italian? Greek? Puerto Rican? Egyptian?" Interestingly, white people wanted to make me out to be anything but black. And black people knew I was half black the moment they saw me. The craziest thing of all was that I didn't even know. I had no proof. My adoption was closed. But my gut, my soul, and everything about me knew that I was half black.

I didn't care about race because my orientation was such that it precluded me from making distinctions based on color. When you are already of mixed ethnicity how could you possibly care what color somebody is? This was the thing I loved most about being bi-racial. I never judged another human being for anything else other than the content of their character.

Myself, I could have been guilty of being a bit aloof on the exterior, but it was only teenage bravado. Under it all, I was as gentle as the petal of a rose.

Mrs. Jordan's journalism class was my favorite. I liked the way I could be free to express myself in crafting a story because I never learned to verbalize my feelings growing up. I was way too careful for that. But writing was completely different. In fact, if someone were to read some-thing I wrote they would never guess it to be from me. They were two different languages entirely. Always, I could find joy on the other side of sorrow. By being afraid as a child, I didn't speak up much. But that gave me an incredible ability to write down my feelings and express myself with the pen.

After reviewing one of my compositions, Mrs. Jordan came beside my desk near the end of class and mentioned, "Bobby, your writing skills are excellent. If you'd like to consider it, I would like you to be the editor of the school newspaper's sports page."

"I'd really love to take that responsibility, Mrs. Jordan."

"Good then. You can get started by writing a feature for the next edi-tion. I'd like you to write a piece on drugs in professional sports."

I did a piece on a professional basketball player whose career ended prematurely because of his addiction to cocaine. It ran on the front page of the sports section of our school newspaper the following week. Seeing my name on the bi-line felt incredible. I was responsible for the article and its contents. It was the first time in my life that I gained esteem from something other than baseball. The best thing about it was that writing was effortless for me. When I heard words, I always remembered them and searched for ways to use them in their proper context. I knew there was power in words, and whenever I came across a word that I didn't understand it irritated me enough to stop every-thing I was doing and look it up in the dictionary. The self-esteem garnered from writing was cerebral in nature, whereas, the feeling I got from accomplishment on the baseball diamond was exhilaration. I made the distinction quickly. Mrs. Jordan encouraged me to take typ-ing the following semester to enhance my skill set for writing.

"With your fingers on the home row keys, you may begin typing." John Ruffo had said it a thousand times. He was my typing teacher and the statistician for the baseball team. I knew him from baseball, and he seemed pleasantly surprised to see me in his classroom. The class was made up of mainly females. I really enjoyed the class because I knew that with this skill, I could take my ideas and immediately trans-fer them to paper faster than I could ever write them down.

At midterms, I waited for him to repeat his mantra before I let loose with my fingers flying all over the keys. The test was simple, type as many words per minute with as few mistakes as possible. I was astonished when I typed 56 words per minute with only 3 errors. It was enough to pull down an 'A'. I felt like I had something. I was really proud. When I showed my parents, their enthusiasm was mild at best. Academic accomplishment was appreciated, but it was not the thing that really moved them. Working on cars or being able to do a tune-up ranked higher. I didn't even want to get dirt under my fingernails. Ivo Bannister didn't know what to do with me. He had only finished the eighth grade in Phillip, South Dakota. After that he quit school and joined the military. He didn't see the value in academics. He needed tangible, hands-on results, sweat on your brow. This irritated me. I wanted congratulations. I wanted some constructive reinforcement, someone to offer me some direction. A way to take the tools I was developing and offer me suggestions as to how to enhance them and put them into practice. But I had learned to think for myself long before. I was always going to be on my own in their home. I wanted to go to college, and I knew that I would have to get there on my own initiative with my own funding. I knew as a sophomore in high school that I needed a scholarship of some sort to make that dream happen.

After a week of spring baseball tryouts, my hamstrings were sore, my arm was sore, and I was on the bubble. My freshman year had been terrific. I started at second base and hit .350. There were five of us who were invited to try out for the varsity. Coach Joe Faccone, who had been the school's only baseball coach in its history, asked me to change positions. He'd like to see me at third base. The only state championship in the school's history belonged to coach Faccone's 1973 club, the team that my older brother, Floyd, starred for. Needless to say, Coach knew me well. He had an all-conference third baseman returning that season for his senior year. The guy was so much more mature than I was. He had a mustache and I hadn't found a razor yet. But I had pedigree. I was competitive, and I knew I was good.

Cuts were posted on Coach Faccone's classroom door the first week of March. I didn't bother looking at the cuts. Instead I went straight to the roster to find my name. It wasn't there. I looked down and saw that I had been cut. I was on the junior varsity roster. The other four guys I had played with as freshman made the varsity—all of them. My peer group was no longer that, and I knew I was better than all four of them. I couldn't believe it! Coach called me into his office anticipating my displeasure. "Bobby, listen son. You'd just sit if I carried you on the roster because Trautmann is All-Conference. You need to get some at bats on the junior varsity."

I did everything I could to stop the water from pooling up in my eyes. My throat was stuck. I could barely talk. When I did, I surprised myself.

"Coach Faccone. When I am a senior, I will be the MVP of this team, the batting champion of this team, and first team all NPSL. Count on it."

I turned and left his classroom where I encountered a group of guys who were trying to be sympathetic towards me. I marched through them and went home.

I was glad that I was angry. That emotion can carry one quite a long way at times. I told my parents at dinner, and they were very surprised.

I sat in my homeroom class later that month and heard Principal John Goodwin announce over the intercom system—"We're proud to announce that Floyd Bannister, a Kennedy alumnus, has just been traded from the Houston Astros to our Seattle Mariners." I was thrilled that my brother would be coming home. Everybody looked at me. I was happy. But I was embarrassed to have been cut. I had these gigantic shoes to fill. I went to a place that I knew very well. I went back inside of myself. I had to summon the warrior's spirit inside to prevail.

I went to junior varsity and 'tore the pitching up.' "They want you on varsity for the last week of the season Bobby," my coach said to me. I dressed for the last five games and got a couple of at-bats.

We routinely had school assemblies. The entire student body must attend and Mass would be said. During Mass, I frequently let my mind wander back to thoughts of my biological mother and father. I usually said a prayer directly to God to let me know who they were so that I could know who I was. Most kids snickered, or passed notes. But I used the time to meditate. Over and over I would tell myself that one day I would find them. I also used the time to think about my future and how to get there. My grade point average was just that; average. I wasn't going to be able to receive an academic scholarship. I had to excel in baseball. It consumed about every moment except for my writing. I realized I needed to use it as my ticket to college.

Junior year, we finished third in the state. We had the talent to win the state championship, but the senior class partied the night before our semifinal game. Our seniors were throwing up in the dugout moments before the first pitch. I went three for four off of a kid who would eventually make it to the major leagues. But we lost 5-3.

The following year was different. Our team was not as good. But I was having a season to remember. I was on a mission. I remembered every word I had said to Joe Faccone in his classroom two years earlier.

From the opening game of the year to the end of the season, everything went right. I homered in the opener and got off to a great start. I ended up the year leading the team in five offensive categories: home runs, doubles, runs batted in, batting average, and on base percentage. My batting average for the season was .405. It was a school record. And I finished second in the North Puget Sound League overall. I was voted first team all NPSL too. I knew I had succeeded in two of the three promises I had made myself and Coach Faccone on that maddening day two years earlier. The team later voted me MVP, and I had the trifecta. I was proud of myself. It proved that I could do anything that I wanted to do. I just had to want it.

Graduation day was hot. I was sweating underneath my graduation gown. Many of the kids at school treated this day like it was really something special. To me it wasn't because I was determined to continue my education. But for some in the crowd, this was it. They were done. It was off to work, whatever was available, and shared apartments with kegs of beer and parties.

I reflected as I waited for my name to be called to receive my diploma. I made some great friends at Kennedy but it was mostly about baseball for me. I dated here and there, but never seriously. Guys in the locker room would talk about girls they had had sex with and it always amazed me. I never let them know, because I had never been with a girl that way. I went all the way through high school without doing 'it'. My Catholic upbringing had much to do with my reluctance. I thought that I would burn in hell, just like the nuns said, if I had intercourse before marriage. But I was also shy. That could wait anyway.

After I received my diploma, I returned to my seat and waited until the festivities concluded. Then I looked for my family and maneuvered through the crowd to see them. To my complete surprise, there was a very familiar face standing alongside my mom and dad. It was Molly! She had been in attendance for my high school graduation. I couldn't believe my eyes. It had been five years since I last saw her. She hadn't changed much but I had changed a lot. I was now much taller than she. She looked up at me with the sweetest smile on her face. That angelic quality had not left her.

She had something wrapped up for me. "A graduation gift," she said. I opened it up to find a beautiful leather sports bag. "I hear you're quite the baseball player, Bobby. I thought maybe you could use this."

It was cute to hear her call me Bobby. Not many people called me that anymore, except during ball games.

"It's perfect, Molly. Thank you. It is great to see you," I said.

I never felt totally comfortable in front of my parents while talking with her because in the past it was as though they were on trial. So I sat down on the bleachers in the gymnasium and she sat beside me. "We'll meet you at the car, take your time," my mom said.

"How did you find out about my graduation, Molly?"

"Your sister Linda called me, and I had to come see you. You look just great Bobby. I am so proud of you."

The evidence of her pride was in her words and in her smile, an emotion I never received from my parents. Right then I wished that she was my parent. But I would have to settle for her being my angel.

"Thank you. I can't tell you how great it is to see you. I thought I would never see you again after the adoption hearing." I added, "Not a day has ever gone by when I didn't thank God for you, for watching out for me and caring enough to check on me and ask me if I was okay."

This time she did cry. She hugged me tightly and whispered over and over, "You're a special one, Bobby."

When I told her that I had a baseball scholarship offer from Bellevue Community College, she beamed. I said, "But I don't know that I'll take it because I'm looking at playing Division One with a Pac-Ten school. Eastern has mentioned that they'd pay tuition if I made the team."

Molly got up to say goodbye, hugged me again and said, "I love you. You keep doing what is right. You've always known that. You are a good soul and what a survivor you are." She shook her head back and forth to emphasize her point. "Bobby, I've seen 99 of 100 kids in your situation fail. I've seen them in and out of juvenile detention centers, I've seen arsonists, sexually promiscuous teenagers, abusers and abused; you name it and I've seen it all. But you are something else. You've got enough intestinal fortitude for all of us. Go out and keep it up Bobby. I will never, ever forget you."

I told her those were the kindest words anyone had ever told me. And I told her I would stay in touch. Then it was goodbye. I knew I would never see her again. If I hadn't actually touched her, I might have mistaken her for an angel, an apparition, a dream. All around me kids were hooting and hollering, throwing their caps as high in the air as they could. I was watching a car drive off, with an angel inside of it. I held my gaze until the car was out of sight.

3

RESOLVE

It was such a hot day. One hundred and eighteen degrees is what the reader board in front of the Bank of America showed. That seemed impossible unless you had experienced a summer in Phoenix. And enduring one hundred and eighteen degrees on a bicycle was almost unthinkable.

I pedaled as quickly as I could to cover the five miles to work at Harry & Steve's Chicago Sports Bar and Grill in Mesa, Arizona. It was like being inside of a furnace. I could feel the lactic acid coursing through my legs as they pumped the pedals. The thirty minutes it took to get there were hell. I beat myself up all the way there and all the way back, regularly.

Particularly, visions of failed opportunities in baseball haunted me. I had been to three different universities chasing my dream of playing professionally: Eastern Washington University, Bellevue Community College, and finally Arizona State University. I was not drafted due to numerous factors: not playing well at the right moments in front of scouts, politics, and worst of all a lack of total effort.

My passion burned brightly at first then faded. Nonetheless, I was done.

I bounced from job to job not liking any of them. And I was so poor that all I had to eat in my studio apartment was a jar of peanut butter and a loaf of bread. The tips I made as a waiter went under the mattress so I could pay my rent. I hated my life, but I didn't know quite what to do to change things either. I was as close as I had ever been to losing my will. What I needed was a vision, something to help me realize my potential and overcome obstacles.

My shift at Harry & Steve's ended at 11:00 p. m. The temperature outside still stood at ninety-eight degrees. On my way home, I stopped by Burger King for a break from the heat. I sat by myself in the fast-food restaurant. The air conditioning was a welcome relief.

In the corner sat a malnourished, unkempt man who was staring at me over his cup of coffee. He looked homeless. I felt distraught: I felt as lost as he looked. I felt like I was dying. I kept blaming my station in life on my past, on being orphaned, and it was threatening to get the best of me.

Then something wonderful happened. I got angry—angrier than ever before. Angrier than when I was cut from the baseball team in high school. And curiously, I began to feel better.

There was a difference between tears of sorrow and tears of anger.

How could I be in my mid twenties, with no car, no girlfriend, a nothing job, and virtually no hope? I had forgotten who I was—the warrior that made it through a frightening childhood.

And it happened right then and there. I made my stand that evening, in that restaurant: I was going to find my biological mother first thing in the morning.

I had talked and talked about finding her, over and over again but never had I done anything to realize it. I used her absence as my crutch. Too often, I used it for self-pity. That night I crossed the line: never ever again did I want to hear myself say, "*If only I knew who my mother and father were, then my life would be better.*"

I was going to make my actions count, and I would not falter in my determination. I resolved that until the moment that I was looking into my mother's eyes, I was going to create the poetry of my life with toughness and determination. I had realized that with each passing twenty-four hours, the time to realize achievement becomes more and more precious.

Something inside of me told me I might know unexpected happiness. But I also might know the sorrow of seeing what was dearest to me cut down before my very eyes. I decided I could accept that. That uncertainty seemed to be the way life presented itself: I had no more time left to buffer this fact with fairy tales, pity, or illogical explanations.

Nine a.m. couldn't come fast enough. I dialed directory services and asked for the number of the Catholic Children's Service's Orphanage in Seattle. I wasn't even sure if it was still in operation. The operator answered and gave me the number. I dialed and asked the receptionist for Molly Johnson. The receptionist apologized and said Molly hadn't been there for a few years. "Can you tell me how I might go about searching for my biological parents?" She told me to call the Washington Adoptive Rights Movement (W.A.R.M.) and ask for Carol Vandenboss. I was happy to be off of work that day because I was on a mission. I was going to call anybody and everybody if I had to. Just taking action made me feel better about my life.

Before I made the call to Carol, I went to the closet and pulled out my briefcase. It was a college graduation gift and it was where I kept my important papers. I dug out my birth certificate, which my parents had given me the day I left their home for Eastern Washington University. Underneath the birth certificate were a few photos they gave me as well. I had asked them for any baby pictures because my intuition told me I would never live in that house again once I stepped foot off of the front porch.

My birth certificate was not the ordinary certificate by any means. In the space where the child's name is to be indicated were the words, "Infant Boy". "Pierre" was written beside that with a black sharpie pen. Beside the space to indicate the father's name it simply said, "Unknown". And beside Mother, it read, "Marianne." Her last name was there too, but it had been blotted out with a black felt pen. I had studied that a thousand times with all the intensity my eyes could muster, holding it to the light. I could almost make out some letters but nothing coherent. It was frustrating to be that close to having an identity.

I dialed the number to W.A.R.M., expecting a web of bureaucracy; however, I asked for Carol Vandenboss and was put directly through to her.

She had a kind voice. She explained that she had been helping facilitate adoptee reunions for nearly 15 years. Carol herself had been through the process of finding her biological mother and it impacted her so greatly that she decided to work for W.A.R.M. in the capacity of an intermediary, or liaison. In no uncertain terms, she explained to me the emotional upheaval involved in what I was asking. There was no way of knowing what I might find. Worse, the reality might be that—even if Carol was able to find her—my mother may not even want to meet me.

"Robert, it is important for you to know how this process works," Carol said. "First, we must petition the court for your birth documents and hope that the judge will release them to us. If so, then I use the information provided therein to begin to search for your mother. If I'm able to locate her, I then give her the choice of whether or not she'd like to proceed and actually meet with you. I give absolutely no identifying information to you or her until I've gotten consent from both of you to proceed with a meeting."

That sounded perfect to me. In fact, I wanted to preserve her privacy to the extent that it would be her choice. Something inside me knew that she would want to meet me if given the opportunity. Call it arrogance or self-assurance, or unwarranted optimism even, but I knew. I knew.

"How long does all of this typically take?" I asked.

"Well, I've seen cases come together as quickly as one month or as long as three years or more. And I have some that are still pending. People can be very tough to find sometimes, Robert."

"Well, I want to start right now. Tell me what I need to do on my end," I said.

"Start by sending $175.00 to W.A.R.M. That covers the cost of filing petitions with the King County Court system. Then you can give me a call about every two weeks so that I can keep you updated as to progress."

I promised to do as she asked and Carol wished me the best of luck. Knowing that I had started the process was a giant relief in itself. The ball was rolling. Granted, it was a heavy ball and I was pushing it uphill, but it was rolling nonetheless.

At times, my optimism was my own worst enemy because I would call every two weeks and get the same answer from Carol. "Call back in two weeks, and we'll see if anything has changed," she would say. The weeks turned to months and my frustration grew to the point where I was no longer calling every two weeks. Instead, I was calling once per month. One day, I was almost to the point where I was going to ask Carol for a refund. But she gave me some hope.

"Robert, the judge who presides over these cases has been on vacation most of the summer. That's why we've been held up in court for so long waiting to get your birth records released. In addition, we're waiting in line behind other cases. It's like a long line at the border," she laughed.

"Okay Carol, I'll just be patient and start calling every six weeks."

On my daily trek to work on that dreaded bicycle I reminded myself that life had to go on around the excitement at the prospect of finding my mother. I was like a hermit though. I went to work and to the library. I had no television at home so I read and read all of the time. I read everything by Richard Wright and Langston Hughes, two of the most prominent black authors. I wanted to know all about black history. And in the mean-time, I pedaled and pedaled in the Arizona heat.

As an almost cruel reminder, each day I would pedal past an auto dealership. There was a car that I wanted, and I could see the price listed in big bold letters on the windshield. I started counting my money under my mattress everyday until I was really close to being able to afford it. Then one day, I counted enough! I could afford to buy that car, and it was still there. It hadn't yet sold.

It had mocked me everyday as I had pedaled away my pounds. I was as light as I had been since my high school days: skinny, but I was in great shape.

On my next day off, I headed out to the dealership. I rode my bike, but I didn't let the salesmen see me coming. I laughed out loud at the hilarity of my situation: I was riding a bike to an auto dealership to buy a car! *"How hilarious,"* I laughed, *"and how humbling."* I took a side road and parked my bike in back of the dealership. I test-drove the car and thought I had gone to heaven. It had air conditioning, and it drove perfectly. There would be no bargaining, no back and forth, because I simply pulled out all of the cash I had to put down and said, "I'll take it."

The salesman asked if I'd like it delivered to my house so that I could drive my car home. I laughed to myself. My car was a Schwinn, and I didn't think I'd ever ride a bike again the rest of my life. It could sit there for all I cared: my trade-in.

I drove and drove all day in my new car and I felt a sense of accomplishment. It was a lesson in patience—a character builder. But the thing about that new car was that it opened up other job opportunities for me because I could only ride that bike so far. Now, I could get the job I really wanted even if it were miles away.

Working for an airline was appealing to me. I scanned the classifieds and saw that Southwest Airlines was hiring ramp agents. I thought that the benefits of flying for free would be incredible and would afford me the opportunity to travel. I interviewed and quickly was hired. There were about one hundred guys working on the tarmac, and most of them were great guys. It was fun pushing the airplanes out onto the runway and loading and unloading baggage. I was making a lot of new friends and life was looking much better to me.

The money wasn't great, but I had the ability to pick up overtime almost whenever I wanted it. So I did. I didn't have much of a social life at that point so I just worked and worked all of the time.

There were only three other black guys out of one hundred on the ramp. And they all quickly befriended me: Big Daddy, Chris Henry (Hendu), and Murra. It was funny how on my first day on the job, Chris Henry came up to me in the break room and said with a giant smile, "You half, ain't you bro?" I nodded and Chris hollered across a crowded lunchroom at Big Daddy, "Yo big daddy, we got three and one half up in this place now."

Big Daddy was an ex-N.F.L. lineman who had played with Minnesota. He was about three hundred and fifty pounds, and he was the man on that ramp—minority or not. Big Daddy answered Chris, "Look here Hendu: we're gonna round up and call it four." He laughed, and so did Chris and I. I was taken in on my first day and felt great about it.

I hadn't heard from Carol in months, and I hadn't bothered calling either. I had almost resigned myself to the fact that the search for my mother might never come to fruition, when one night near the end of a double shift I was paged to the supervisor's office. I was in my fourteenth or fifteenth straight hour of work and feeling dog tired from a long, long day in the sun. I was daydreaming about this new stereo system I was going to get for my car. The page startled me because I recognized it as being rare. Usually guys were paged to the office for disciplinary reasons or to be awarded overtime for the following day. But I had not signed up for overtime, nor had I done anything wrong. So I quickly moved into the supervisor's office where a crowd of five or six night shift guys were milling around. Steve Dombroski, the manager, waved me in and said I had a long distance call from Seattle and that it was urgent. He said it was a woman named Carol Vandenboss holding for me on line two. My heart began to beat quickly. Why would she be calling me in the evening at work? It must be important. Could she have found her? I felt my head get light, and my legs felt like they weren't quite under me. I sat and took the call.

"Robert, I have just great, great news for you. I have found your mother. Her name is Marianne Kuhn, and she will be calling you in the morning. She is thrilled and can't wait to speak with you."

I smiled and smiled, and I thanked her. I made her swear to me that it was not a dream.

"Oh my God Carol, I can't believe it. You did it. Thank you so much."

All of the guys around me knew something big was up. They saw my eyes tear up and I put my head into my hands and just wept. Steve asked all of the guys to get out of his office while I regained my composure. I explained to him that I began looking for my mother two years prior and had never so much as seen a photo of her or my father. I told him I was about to speak to her for the first time in my life the following morning. "Steve, I'm 27 years old, man. And I'm going to meet my mother tomorrow."

He was awed by it all.

"Banny, that is incredible, man. It's like something from a talk show. I'll tell you what big guy, you take tomorrow off paid. It's on me."

"Thanks Steve, I really appreciate that."

"Good luck, and why don't you go tell the guys your good news? Those guys think the world of you, ya' know."

Part II

THE CHOOSER OF ROADS

*"I have learned this at least by my experiment: that if one advances confidently in
the direction of his dreams, and endeavors to live the life which he has imagined,
he will meet with a success unexpected in common hours."*

HENRY DAVID THOREAU

4

BREAKTHROUGH

THERE was magic in the air that evening as I paced around my apartment full of energy. The sheer force of my will had brought about the manifestation of a lifelong dream. This was a heady feeling. I couldn't eat. And when it came time to sleep I couldn't do that either. My mind raced with thoughts of my mother. I knew that I would engage myself fully with her. I was not going to ever let her get away from me again. It's hard to imagine that something as innocuous as a conversation with someone over the telephone could be so life-changing. I was nearing the defining moment of my life.

At five a. m. the telephone rang. It was her. Carol had informed me that Marianne would be calling me early in the morning. I hadn't slept much at all that evening. I immediately sat straight up in my bed, threw off the covers and raced to the phone. I was very light-headed. I had never, ever, been this nervous when I had stepped into the batter's box with the game on the line. Nor was I ever this nervous when my college final exam was placed in front of me. The feeling could only be likened to an altered state: suspended animation. Complete exhilaration.

I picked up the receiver, "Hello." What came through that receiver was the sound of healing, empowerment, redemption, and most of all pure love.

"Hello Robert, this is Marianne."

It was her tone that put me at ease. It was soft and gentle, maybe even somewhat frightened.

"Hi, Mom," I answered back.

It was thrilling to be able to say those two words with conviction, and to know she really was mine. She liked the fact that I called her

Mom right away. The way that she called me 'Robert' made me never want to be called 'Bob' again. It sounded so nice coming from her.

"Mom, would you describe what you look like to me? Because I don't look like anybody else I've ever known."

"Well, I've got red hair and blue eyes and I'm about five feet, five inches," she answered.

A redhead! I laughed to myself. I had always imagined her to be very tall and brunette for some reason. But she was a petite little red head. I was amazed. She sounded so young to me, so naturally my next question came quickly.

"How old are you?"

I knew you were never supposed to ask a woman her age, but I supposed this was the perfect exception to the rule.

"I had you when I was eighteen Robert, so that would make me forty-five; and you must be twenty- seven."

She was so young. She was younger than my oldest sister. She was twenty years younger than my parents. It was mind-blowing. My next question was the biggie. I wanted to know about my father in the worst way.

"Mom, can you tell me about my father?" I asked.

Her answer made me drunk with self-realization. It was like I had never existed and now I was being put together piece by piece. God was introducing me to myself.

"Well Robert, your father is something else. He was an incredibly talented musician. I met him in Vancouver, British Columbia at the Harrison Hot Springs Resort where he was performing. He's black, and he's from the Caribbean island of Haiti."

I was hanging on her every single word, on every syllable. I was a man who had never eaten a meal and was suddenly presented a feast.

"His native language is French, but he's fluent in four or five languages; he had traveled all over the world. And he is so handsome."

I asked her what he looked like.

"That's hard to describe," she sighed. "But off of the top of my head I would say that he looks a little bit like the actor Danny Glover, or maybe like Sidney Poitier."

We talked that morning for over three hours and the time seemed to just fly right by. It was fun to be able to tell her all about my life and to find out about hers. She had grown up and lived about twenty minutes from me. To think back on all of those times when I was in agony over being without her, and she was just a short drive away, was so ironic.

To talk with my mom was great, but I wanted to see her as quickly as possible. I let her know that I worked for an airline and that I could fly for free anytime she wanted me to go up to Seattle.

"Oh, my kids Dean and Chrissy are going to want to meet you too Robert."

We made plans to meet in the following weeks and after a long time on the phone, we said goodbye to each other.

"Mom, I just wanted you to know something before we get off of the phone. I have always loved you."

"I love you too, Robert."

I wished she could have reached through the phone that moment and held me like a baby. I would have let her. I needed to know what that sort of affection felt like because I had never received it nor given it to another human being. I kept a space inside my heart locked up just for her and it went unused for twenty-eight years. I needed desperately to learn what being loved felt like.

We exchanged addresses and promised to write each other often until we met. She attempted to explain to me several times what precipitated her having to give me up for adoption, but each time I steered the subject a different direction because I wasn't looking for any explanations or apologies…just love. All I wanted from my mother was her love.

And she was so loving. She had the sweetest, kindest voice in the world. It was my impression, in as much as a phone conversation can reveal, that she was a really good person.

It was difficult for either of us to say goodbye and hang up the telephone, but we finally did. My ears were sore from the pressure of the receiver. I set the phone down and got up off the sofa. I began to walk towards the kitchen and everything got blurry. Tears came raining down uncontrollably. I made my way down to my knees to pray. I hadn't been on my knees in prayer since my days as an altar boy. I folded my hands together and repeated several times, maybe even one hundred times,

thank you, thank you, thank you.

When I boarded the Alaska Airlines Boeing 737, I showed my non-revenue pass to the flight attendants and they indicated that I wouldn't have to wait to board because there were plenty of seats available.

One of them asked me whom I flew for and I told her that I wasn't a flight attendant but that I worked in ground operations for Southwest Airlines.

"I'm flying up to Seattle today to meet my mother for the first time in my life, if you can believe that," I told her.

She was thrilled for me and immediately moved me up to first class.

"Follow me and I'll seat you up in first class so that you can be the very first person off of the plane," she said.

I thanked her and collected my things to put away in the overhead bin.

"You must be so incredibly nervous," she added.

"Well, I'm not the nervous type but yes, you could say that."

During the flight I looked at all of my pictures that I had gathered to show her. It was a snapshot of my youth complete with grade-school photos and pictures of me playing baseball. I had gone out and bought myself a suit to wear for the occasion too.

If there is one word people would use to describe me, anybody who knew me well, that is, it is probably 'relaxed', or if two words, 'laid back'. That, however, was not the case when the aircraft touched down onto the runway and the pilot slowly taxied the plane into gate D-9. The two and one half hour flight had seemed to take forever, and I was growing more and more nervous by the moment.

The flight attendant opened the door as the jet way extended to meet the airplane, and then she looked at me and excitedly motioned for me to deplane first. I was frozen in my seat. I couldn't move. I needed to breathe and regain my composure, so I told her to let the other passengers go ahead of me. I waited until every single passenger was off of the airplane before I rose and gathered my things.

With a deep breath, I relaxed and reassured myself that she loved me.

I thanked the attendant and started around the corner up the jet way. I reached the top of the jet way and moved through the open doorway. In our correspondence over the last few weeks, I had sent her a photograph of myself, but I had no photos of her. I had only her description to go by, but I hoped that she would be able to recognize me first. There was only one person left in the waiting area, and we looked at each other simultaneously. She stood still, wearing a white sundress. The closer I got the faster I walked until I was within a few feet of her.

She had the most beautiful blue eyes I had ever seen, and they were twinkling with excitement as I reached out for her.

"Hi, Mom," I said as I hugged her tightly to me.

She buried her head into my chest, and I could feel her trembling before she said the most tender words to me.

"Robert, I hope you don't hate me for what I did to you."

Her bottom lip quivered with every difficult word she had just said to me.

"I have never, ever hated you. Not once ever. I have always loved you."

The words were like a wave washing over her, calming her.

We walked through the airport together. It was fascinating for me just to watch my mother walk. I was studying her every movement, from the shape of her forearms to the lines that ran from her nose to the corners of her mouth.

I recognized myself in her.

She was looking at me the same way, with incredible electricity in her eyes. She had a sparkle in her blue eyes that made me imagine someone had scooped up a handful of water from the South Pacific Ocean and poured it into her eyes. Magnificently blue.

We entered the parking garage and as we neared her car, Marianne began to look in her purse for her car keys. She found them and offered them to me. She extended her arm and her hands were literally shaking.

"Robert, would you mind driving? I'm a little too nervous to drive right now."

I told her that would be fine and we got in the car. She had a brand new convertible and the top was down. It struck me how young she was. Not just her appearance but her energy and enthusiasm. She had a vibrancy about her that was palpable. I really liked the way I felt while I was in her presence. I felt natural. I was far more comfortable than she was, but I knew she would relax after a while.

She was so very light in complexion. She had freckles and red hair. I was dark brown - darker than usual because of the summer sun in Phoenix. I was like a twelve-minute oven-baked biscuit. The longer I was in the sun, the browner I got.

The date was June 5th, 1989: a date I will never forget. It became my second birthday and Mother's Day all at once, the date on which I found my mother.

We talked as we drove, looking for a place to stop and eat lunch. We stopped at a restaurant and the hostess seated us. The waitress came to take our order and I blurted out, "This is my mom. We just met each other about ten minutes ago." I couldn't help myself. I wanted to tell the whole world that I had found my mother and to show everyone how proud I was of her.

Marianne barely ate anything so I offered to eat her lunch as well as my own. She laughed and was amazed by my appetite. She would later learn to practically guard her food when I was around.

"You don't think I got to be this size skipping meals, do you, Mom?" I joked.

She giggled. Her laugh was so cute. We were both silly, even goofy in a way. There were two noticeable traits that we shared, and I picked up on them within hours of meeting her. First was our silly nature. We both really liked to laugh a lot, and we had the same sense of humor. Second, neither of us had any sense of direction.

I couldn't help but contemplate the argument of environment versus heredity. I was like a case study of it. Your environment will certainly shape you, and your experiences inside of that environment will help mold your character, but your environment cannot ever influence your nature. And to fully understand your nature, it helps to see it in someone else and have them recognize it in you as well. This was happening during our lunch, and I loved it. I was beginning to live, and that may well have been the first day of my entire life in which I was filled, overflowing, with happiness.

Marianne had planned a party for me at her sister Gayle's house later that evening. We went home and changed clothes before we left for the party. Just before we arrived, I had to pull over to the side of the road and stop the car. I put my head on my mom's shoulder and couldn't stop myself from crying. She held onto me so sweetly and comforted me. Where she may have been nervous, I was emotional. It overwhelmed me at that moment that she was sitting two feet away from me. Not an apparition. She really, really was right there. Now I was moments away from meeting more family members whom she had gathered together just to meet me. I was going to meet aunts, uncles, cousins, and my half brother and sister. And her husband.

Walking through the crowded house was surreal. Everyone was looking at me. And everybody was really nice, especially Marianne's two aunts who were there. They were spoiling me with attention and made me feel very, very welcome. I stayed close to my mom, almost shadowing her every move. We held hands. She introduced me to everyone with such pride that it made me feel great inside. I was quickly made aware of what a sweet person my mom was by testimonial after testimonial from all of my newfound relatives. They raved about her. I could already tell what they were talking about, but it was nice to have my first impressions of her confirmed by all of my relatives.

My brother Dean and sister Chrissy were there. Dean was shorter than I, but very thickly built. He was a little on the quiet side but really nice to me. Chrissy was more animated for sure, a real character. She was vivacious, and in that respect, reminded me a lot of Marianne. She was very petite and lively. She was definitely full of energy. And she seemed much more comfortable around me than Dean was. It was great knowing I had a new brother and sister. I looked for similarities in our appearance and found it in our eyes.

Marianne's husband Ken, welcomed me with a handshake and then quickly moved on to talk with someone else. It was cordial, but not a warm welcome. It seemed like he was the only one at the party who wasn't really happy about me being there. I wasn't sure though, until he called Marianne over to talk.

"I'll be right back, Robert," she said to me as she squeezed my hand firmly in hers.

While I spoke to another relative, I watched out of the corner of my eye. Ken and Marianne had an animated discussion in the corner. It was not pleasant, that much I knew. They turned their backs on one another and the normally joyous appearance on my mother's face had turned angry.

"Is everything all right?" I asked when she returned.

"Yes, he's just being…," and she couldn't think of the word to describe him, so she just left it at that with exasperation.

"What's the matter?" I asked.

"He just asked me what in the hell does your father look like?"

A chill came over the room and descended right on me. It came again rearing its ugly head: race. Just when I thought that the world was right. Months had gone by without race being an issue, then it surfaced without the slightest warning, putting me back on my heels yet again.

"Listen to me Mom, I love you, but here's what I'm going to do. I'll go back to Phoenix tomorrow morning because I never intended to be a cause of any problems for you."

Her reply was a testimony to her inner strength and her love for me. The bluntness of her statement shocked me.

"Robert, I will divorce him before I let you go."

I couldn't believe it. But I actually did believe her because her eyes were intense. She was angry and, boy, what a look she had on her face.

"This party sucks, let's get out of here," she added.

I agreed. I was going wherever she was going. I thought to myself, *what a woman. Here is one strong -willed woman.* I really liked what I saw from her. She was not to be messed with for sure. I never had that kind of a temper my whole life. I was always too frightened of the repercussions of an outward display of anger. But I was as passive-aggressive as they come. If someone angered me I simply would never give them the time of day again. They wouldn't see me, nor would they ever hear my voice again. They became dead to me. I was envious of Marianne's ability to catch on fire the way she did. *My mother, the red-headed firecracker,* I mused.

Back inside the comfort zone of her car, she filled in the gaps for me.

"You know Robert, when I first married Ken, I told him that I had a child whom I had to put up for adoption. But I did not tell him your father is black. He didn't ask. And I didn't find it relevant anyway."

Ken saw me standing beside her, six-foot three- inches and dark brown from the Phoenix summer. He saw me beside his five-foot five-inch, red headed, freckled, Norwegian wife, and he blew a gasket.

"Well, hopefully he'll get past all of that nonsense when he has a chance to get to know me better," I said.

"I don't care about him. Let's go have some fun," she said with the familiar smile returning to her face.

That night, outside of a waterfront restaurant, I fell asleep standing up, inside my mother's arms. We were hugging, but it was so tender that I just melted inside of her arms and nodded off. I never slept with such peace in my entire life. It was the kind of slumber that babies must enjoy everyday. It was the first time I felt safe in twenty-eight years. I was where I belonged.

When Marianne woke me, I was shocked that I could have fallen asleep in her arms, standing up! I underestimated my need for affection because I simply didn't quite know what it was. I was enlightened by the tenderness of love. And it was bittersweet. I suddenly had the explanation to all of my failed relationships. Every relationship I ever attempted was fractured in some way. If I had not experienced the incomparable tenderness of a mother's love, then how in the world could I accept it from another woman? I couldn't and didn't. If it came to me, I ran from it even though love was the thing I craved the most. Like a 'eureka' moment, suddenly I understood myself better.

"Was I snoring?" I sheepishly asked.

"Yeah, you sure were Robert," she said.

I apologized and slowly let go of my embrace. That night I went back home to the house where I was raised. What a day I'd had! I slept comfortably that night knowing that the next thing I must do was tell Ivo and Ione Bannister that I had found my biological mother. Before telling anyone, I had wanted to meet her and be certain that we were going to be a part of each other's lives.

Ivo and Ione were vacationing in South Dakota and were very surprised to get a long distance call from me. Since I had moved from the house, we really only spoke during the holiday season. Their surprise was apparent when they answered the phone.

"Hi Bobby, what's the occasion? Are you getting married?"

"Well no, it's more important than that actually," I replied.

They were quiet on the other end of the phone.

"Last night I met my biological mother, Marianne Kuhn, for the first time. Before you say anything I just wanted you to be the first to know and to understand that this decision was made completely independent of you. Nothing you did or did not do led me to this. This was for me. I needed it. And you already did your job with me. You raised me well, and I will always recognize that fact."

I wanted them to be happy for me, to respond like mature adults who were genuinely interested in what made their son happy. That was asking too much. They acted like I had told them I just finished washing the dishes.

"Okay then Bobby, good for you. We hope you're happy."

There was not a hint of surprise, or support. Just detached, false congratulations. I hung up the phone vowing not to let them ever make me feel guilty about my decision. I would never feel that. I had seen them play the guilt game with all of their biological kids. They made the conscious choice to assume the responsibilities that go with parenting. I believed that parenting was a privilege, not a task. And to make your child feel like you sacrificed or they owe anything at all, was ludicrous and ignorant. There is a poignant moment in the film, *Guess Who's Coming to Dinner* as Sidney Poitier is chastised by his father for wanting to marry a white woman. His father asks him how he could do such a thing to him and his mother after all of the sacrifices they had made for him. Sidney Poitier's character responds brilliantly, verbally dressing down his father by telling him that he owes him nothing. "You owed me everything you could possibly give me the moment I was born," he answers defiantly. I agree completely, but I should have never expected Ivo and Ione to show me a maturity of emotion that was never before displayed. I didn't care. This was bigger than them.

The next morning, Marianne and I drove by the unwed mothers' home where she had stayed after being kicked out of the house by her father, Einar Nopson. This was incredible to see. It made me feel sad for her. Then she turned and headed a different direction.

"Robert I want to take you somewhere special, if you'd like to go."

"Anywhere you want, Mom."

We pulled into a cemetery. I raised my eyebrows and looked at her.

"This is where your grandparents—my dad, Einar, and mom, Mary—are buried."

Wow! Knowing he never wanted me born was intimidating to say the least, but I held her hand and we walked straight to their gravesite. Marianne laid some flowers down and then simply blurted out, "This is your grandson, Robert. You would have loved him."

I was flabbergasted. I felt like some kind of ancestral breach. Here I was standing above the coffin of my grandfather who had been responsible for the break-up of my own mother and father . He must have been turning in his grave!

Marianne accomplished two things that morning by taking me there. She got a measure of redemption, and she legitimized me not to myself, but to her deceased parents. What a thing for her to do! I was so impressed by her.

Leaving the cemetery, I had some frightening revelations about life. I could so very easily not have been there at that very moment. If Marianne had made a different choice... I calculated what she was up against: an unwed pregnancy, the father black and no longer in the picture, the year 1963. The fact was that in 1963 there were still 18 states holding steadfast to miscegenate laws; she would have been breaking the law in most of the southern states had she even thought of marrying my father. I compared these circumstances to the way things currently were and shook with fear at how conceivable it could have been for me to have never been born. And with these thoughts came a great deal of gratitude and respect for my mother for giving me a chance, at least a crack at life.

People often muse about destiny; however, choices are often made first, in order for destiny to manifest. And on rare occasions, choices intersect at a crossroad leading to such an immensely powerful destiny that generations can be healed. The choices of the son, the mother, and the grandmother and grandfather were transformed that morning. History was rewritten and a better version of it was served that day in the cemetery. I held my mother's hand tightly, hoping to convey all of these thoughts to her in a single squeeze of the hand as we walked out of the front gates together.

5

HEALING

No matter how extreme a situation is, it will change. It can't continue forever. Events balance themselves out by seeking their opposites, and this process of balance is at the heart of all healing.

The process may take time. It depends on the event. If momentous, then it may take years or even lifetimes for things to return to an even keel.

My healing process had just begun. I wished I could hit the fast forward button and be just fine, but the fact remained: I was playing catch up in a big way. I went more than a quarter of a century without the most basic emotional development and bonding. Nobody would know it from looking at me, but I was a scared young man. But like a thoroughbred in the stall, I waited and waited while everybody else lapped me several times over. By the time I joined the race, I was behind by more than a few laps. I was behind by twenty-eight years. But after spending the weekend with my mom, I was ready to run like the wind. It was going to be something to behold. I knew that my life had some drastic changes in store, and that it was just a matter of time before the scales were going to even out and then tip in my favor.

The flight home to Phoenix afforded me time to play back the weekend's events in my mind and marvel at the happiness I was feeling. I felt like a baby. I wanted to please her and to make her proud of me. When I showed her some of my writing including my poetry, she loved it and praised my ability. This was foreign to me, but I loved it. She made me feel good about myself. Best of all was the feeling I got whenever I looked in her eyes. I felt connected to the world. I felt like I had a history, and I did. Before, everything had started and ended with me. I'd had no medical history, no background. That was one very lonely way to go through life. With just one half of the recipe of my existence, I was a changed man.

Despite all that I had on my plate, I knew that what was happening was bigger than I. It reached beyond me. I knew that giving me up had been hard on Marianne, and I understood that, reunited, Marianne and I were healing one another.

I had no meaningful relationships to speak of in Phoenix. They were all fractured. I hadn't let people in far enough to give them the capacity to leave me or hurt me. If I had sensed they wanted in, I had bluntly or passive-aggressively slammed shut the door; whatever tactic fit the drama. The end result was that I was a one-man island. Women had been confounded by me because on one hand I could be more sensitive and forthright than anybody they had ever known, and detach from them completely on a dime. This was dangerous because it stunted my emotional development. Things like trust, honesty, and loyalty were just words to me. I did have some very close platonic friendships wherein these things were a non-issue; however, where intimate relationships were concerned, I was a complete mess.

The moment I got off of the plane in Phoenix my mind began to race with ideas of how I could potentially move back to Seattle. The dilemma was that I hated Seattle. I hated the weather. It was constantly either raining or threatening to rain, and summer consisted of a ten-day period. I was always sick in Seattle. During nine years in Phoenix, I never had allergies or a cold. But for time with Marianne, I would do it. I wanted to be around her all of the time so that I could learn all there was to know about my mom. What I needed was a job in Seattle that afforded me a lot of travel, a way to get away from the dreary weather. It was then that the perfect idea popped into my mind. Instead of throwing baggage into the airplane cargo bins I may as well work in the cabin and stay clean. I saw flight attendants coming and going on airplanes all day long. Every last one of them seemed to love the job. They were traveling for basically no charge and they made more than I did on the ramp while working less--much less, I thought. The only problem was that the company I worked for, Southwest Airlines, did not have a flight attendant base in Seattle. But I knew that Alaska Airlines had a large Seattle base. I saw their planes taxi in every day right across the ramp from me. It always reminded me of home to see that big Eskimo face on the tail. Guys on the ramp were always asking me about Seattle.

It had a reputation of being a great city. I always told them that it was fantastic provided you could tolerate some seriously gray skies.

One morning while on break, I walked across the tarmac and up the stairs to the jet way that was connected to the Alaska aircraft. I was going on a fact-finding mission. I needed to know how much I could earn and if in fact I would be based in Seattle. Up at the top of the jet way, I encountered a trio of flight attendants who were very willing to inform me as to the specifics of the job. They loved it. And best of all, they told me that Alaska was interviewing in Phoenix later that month, and one of the girls knew someone who was on the hiring committee. I gave them my name and told them about finding my mother. They all encouraged me to give it a shot, and they seemed convinced that I would have an excellent chance to be hired.

My roommate at the time was a Southwest flight attendant. Brad was from Missouri and was a really laid back, great guy. He was constantly throwing parties at our apartment and the girls he flew with would come streaming through the front door leaving my jaw on the ground.

"Banny," Brad said, "Whatever you do, don't tell them at the interview that you want the job because you love to travel. They've heard that one a million times. What they're looking for is someone unique, with a different story. Your looks are unique and that will get you past the first group, but throw something at them that they've never heard before and you are in, my man."

"Maybe I should just tell them I want to meet a lot of girls," I joked.

"Yeah, if you want to throw bags on the ramp in one-hundred-degree weather for the rest of your life."

Brad coached me for a few weeks by throwing every possible question at me that he could think of. I was polished and ready with great answers by the time the interview came.

"Guess what Mom?" I smiled into the telephone receiver. "I am interviewing with Alaska Airlines Thursday for a job that will have me based in Seattle."

"Oh goody!"

That always cracked me up when she said that. She was like a little girl on Christmas morning when she said that.

I quickly tempered her enthusiasm saying, "They are hiring a class of forty flight attendants, but they are anticipating over seven-hundred and fifty applicants at the cattle call Thursday."

"But Robert, you know that when they see you they will be left with nothing to do but hire you on the spot. You're so handsome, how could they not hire you?"

"Well Mom, I don't know about that, but I will give it my best shot for sure. That way I can see you all of the time."

She had been to Phoenix to visit me a few weeks after we had first met, and the time just flew by. It wasn't enough. I needed to be around her on a regular basis, and she felt the same way. We had a great time when she came and it was amazing the transformation she had undergone in just a month. She had lost weight and colored her hair. She got off of the plane and I saw several guys looking lustfully at her. Now, that freaked me right out. But she really deserved the looks. She was simply beautiful. It had been heartbreaking to have to say goodbye to her again, but she left knowing that I was going to think of a way to get back to Seattle. Now my thoughts had taken me to the precipice one more time. It's amazing, really, to consider the power that our thoughts have especially when those thoughts are accompanied by action. The world, it seems, can be spun right off its axis.

The Biltmore Hotel lobby was flooded with mostly beautiful, young women in navy or black suits. Sprinkled throughout the crowd was the occasional guy, but not many. Someone mentioned that there were five other big rooms full of applicants. The weeding-out process began immediately as they called us up in alphabetical order. The name Bannister put me in front of a panel very quickly. The first thing they did was measure my height and then take down my weight. The maximum height for a male flight attendant was six feet, three inches. It was set as such because of the specifications of the aircraft's interior. Any taller and the guy wouldn't fit. So I snuck in at the maximum height of six feet, three inches. After assessing that my weight and height were proportionate, they informed me I had made it to one of ten group interviews that would be held in the next hour.

There were to be fifty people in each of the ten group interviews. I did the math quickly.

They were hiring forty to fifty people. That put the odds at five people per class: five out of fifty. Still I was really confident because there weren't many men. Plus I had made it through the hardest part: the subjective portion wherein people were weeded out based only on how they looked.

When they discussed how the group interview would be held I knew I had a terrific chance. The format called for me to partner with the person to my left and tell them the most interesting thing about my life. That person would then stand up and introduce me and my story. At the end of the session, the hiring committee called out the names of those applicants who had been selected for a second interview immediately in an adjacent room. "Robert Bannister," they called out. "Yes," I said under my breath. I was one step closer to getting to know my mom so much better and at the same time not having to be in Seattle all of the time. It was the perfect scenario.

At the end of my second interview I readied myself to shake hands and thank the airline personnel for their time, when I was asked a surprising question.

"Robert, would you be able to fly to Seattle tomorrow morning for a third and final interview with our Director of Inflight Administration?"

"Yes, that would be no problem at all."

They then placed a round trip ticket in my hand and wished me luck. I knew that if I didn't get in my own way, I had the job; otherwise they would never offer to fly me to Seattle. I was very excited at the prospect of moving back now that I had something to move back for. I had been in Phoenix for six years and never gone back to Seattle once until the morning I met Marianne.

Recognizing when to close the book on one chapter of your life and be open to the change that will ensue is the only way to really take measure of your life. I followed my instincts more than anybody I knew, and when I paid close attention to my gut it never betrayed me. My mind and my heart would sell me down the river in a heartbeat, but my gut never lied. From the moment I had sat alone in that restaurant feeling like I was dying and resolving to finally do something about it by taking concrete action, my intuition had been guiding me forcefully enough that I felt like every decision I made was right on the money. An athlete would liken the feeling to being in the zone. My life was 'in the zone.' I knew that to fully realize the potential of one's life, you must put others before yourself. I was putting my mother first and the circumstances were practically laying themselves out for me. I was offered the job with Alaska Airlines. This meant that I would indeed be moving home and could realize my dream of being near Marianne.

I was an actor in the play of life, the way Shakespeare so eloquently portrayed it. The curtain was coming down on Act One of my life, and I was glad for it. I felt sorry for people who surrendered to mundane lives, shunning change as though it were a lethal poison. I embraced change. It reminded me that I was living. I knew that I was in the midst of life's drama, just beginning to grow.

Trying to pick apart my life's path and make sense of it all was overwhelming. I knew three things and I knew them with my gut. First, I knew that I had found my mother. Second, I knew that I loved her and she loved me. Third, I knew that I had to be wherever she was, and that I was going to her.

Driving my little Honda CRX up Interstate 5 through Bakersfield with Seattle as my destination about eighteen hours away, I shook my head back and forth while chuckling at myself. "*Man, you are either the craziest cat in the world to pick up and start all over like this, or the most romantic, courageous man around.*" I was a little bit of both. But how could I be expected to tolerate displeasure as a grown man when my childhood was practically defined by it? Marianne represented happiness to me, and I was driving like a madman to get to that feeling. I only stopped once in Sacramento when my eyes started playing tricks on me while driving. I pulled into a Motel 6 and slept for about two hours before I was back on the road. I made it into Seattle twenty-six hours after leaving Phoenix the prior evening. The drive was symbolic. I was changing jobs, changing climates, and changing lives.

There was no one to blame for my foul mood. But I knew what was bugging me as I reached into my top drawer for a pair of my warmest socks. I was freezing. After ten years in the desert, my blood had thinned considerably and was hardly ready for the shocking change of climate. My covers felt cold and wet. They felt soggy, but I knew they weren't wet. My skin was beginning to lighten out to a sickly shade of olive green. The one factor that saved me from going crazy was my ability to get out of town on a regular basis. I was a couple of months into my flying career at Alaska Airlines, and I was really enjoying it.

The holiday season was approaching fast, and I was looking forward to spending my first Christmas with Marianne. I had a tough transition to make because I was on reserve status with the airline, meaning I only flew intermittently to cover sick calls from other flight attendants. This limited my earning ability profoundly, so much so that I needed to consider alternative living arrangements to fit my budget.

I was talking with my new sister Chrissy one afternoon when she said, "Robert, I think Mom would love to have you live with her for awhile until you can get on your feet."

"Do you really think so Chrissy?" I asked.

She said that she would talk about it with Marianne and let me know. Before I knew it, I was packing my things up and getting ready to move into my mom's house. I knew we would have a blast together; however, I was unsure how Ken, her husband, would receive me. To my relief, he approved and welcomed me into his home. Marianne and I were like the very best of friends. The mother and son relationship was inherent, but we were more like best friends than son and mother. I started flying a bit more so I wasn't often around, but when I was, we talked and talked all of the time. We laughed most of the time.

As Christmas approached, I deliberated over what to get Marianne. I wanted something really special for her, but I was restricted by my budget. I was busy getting back on my feet and out of debt.

One evening I stood in front of the beautiful Christmas tree that Marianne had put up in the front room. We hugged and talked about how special this holiday was to both of us. She was the best gift I could have ever asked for because I found peace in her company. She was so caring and tender. And that evening I went to my room and picked up a pen in order to capture all of the beautiful thoughts that were swirling around in my head. What came forth from that pen in the following thirty minutes was a poem that I didn't so much write as I simply dictated. It popped into my head from some universal source of inspiration. It was my first Christmas gift for Marianne:

Candy canes adorned the great noble fir, While red stockings hung in display. In the reflection of a bulb he was looking for her.

She would stand right before him someday.

Heavenly snowflakes did fall from the sky,

As the baby Jesus heard a young boy's cry,

And sent an angel to dry up the pools in his eyes.

A mother, his wish.

Her heart topped his list.

Wrapped in a ribbon of crystals that reflect the beauty of her soul.

Miracles unfold on Christmas Eve,

And dreams come true you must believe.

A man now stood before the tree,
His mother in his arms.
Like a priceless treasure lost at sea,
I held her close to me.
The gift of love from a mother to her son,
My Christmas gift,
A most precious one.

The pen dropped from my fingertips, satisfied with its work. I hadn't even paused to consider what it sounded like, whether or not it was grammatically correct. I was like a conduit to some wonderful, beautiful place where words grew on trees like roses for the picking.

When I stopped and read what I had written, I was amazed at how sweet it was. I hoped that Marianne would appreciate the state of mind I had to find in order to create this poem for her. It wasn't an expensive gift, but I had given her a real piece of my soul with those words. And best of all, writing it did me just as much good as reading it would hopefully do for her. I was pleased.

To round out the most wonderful Christmas of my life, God didn't stop with simply allowing me to spend it with Marianne, in her home. As I woke early Christmas morning, I looked out the front window to a beautiful scene. It was a white Christmas. Snowflakes were falling everywhere, coming down in waves. It was perfect. Marianne read her poem and directed a smile at me that was wonderful. She had that twinkle in her eye that was so expressive. That morning meant a great deal to me. It was the anniversary of a date that had given me pain deep in my heart every year.

Sure I was pleased to open gifts growing up, but Christmas had been the one day on which I had known I belonged someplace else. Until that Christmas Day, the holiday had mocked me each and every year, a painful reminder of what family is supposed to be.

December 25th, 1989 was different. I was where I belonged, and was looking across the room at the person I belonged to. The scent of the pine needles took on a whole new meaning to me that year, as did the echo of Nat King Cole's spectacular voice. If I were able to express my undiluted joy that morning, I may not have lived through it. I had so much emotion in my heart that to capture it all would be to ask too much of me. It would have drained me of everything I had. Instead, I moved across the room to where Marianne stood and hugged her tightly.

6

OPPORTUNITY

THAT spring, Marianne and I began to put together some plans for a vacation. I was turning thirty years old and I wanted to go someplace warm and celebrate, just the two of us. It would have been easy to go to Mexico because we could have just flown on my company passes for free, but there was something inside of me just itching to go to the Caribbean. I started inquiring amongst all of my co-workers as to the best place to go. On one of my flights we had finished up the service early due to turbulence and retreated to the galley. One of the flight attendants proceeded to tell me all about this trip to Jamaica that she had just taken.

"We stayed right on the beach in these cabins for fifteen dollars per night. The only bad part was that the bathrooms and showers were outside. But oh my god, you wouldn't believe the sunsets," she said.

I straightened right up and asked her the name of the place.

"Ozzie's Shack," she said.

I cracked up.

"What kind of a name is that?"

"You'll see if you go there. I can't explain it. It's very Bohemian."

She still had the phone number in her purse and she gave it to me.

"If you call, ask for Miss Lena, and she'll set you up."

I thanked her and looked for a place in my wallet where I could put the number and not lose it.

"Hey there Red head, do you feel like going to Jamaica mon?" I said to Marianne.

I had gotten in the habit of calling Marianne, 'Red head' and speaking in an alter ego to her. I always clowned around with her and spoke to her like I was an old black man named 'Otis', from the Mississippi Delta. She got a kick out of it.

"Yeah Otis, let's go to Jamaica," she answered without missing a beat and added, "When do we leave?"

"Well first Mom, I'm serious. I just flew with this girl who told me all about this place in Jamaica and it cost, get this, you won't believe this, fifteen dollars per night. I've called the pass bureau and found out that our tickets on American are ninety percent off. We're talking about fifty dollars round trip. Mom, we can go spend a week or so for under two hundred dollars."

"Let's do it!"

"Can you get the time off for my birthday?"

"You bet I can."

She would've left that day if I put a ticket in her hand.

I called the number to Ozzie's Shack to make reservations.

"Hello, may I speak to Miss Lena, please?"

"Dis be Miss Lena mon."

The thick Jamaican accent charmed me.

"Hi, my name is Robert Bannister, and I'd like to make reservations to stay at one of your cabins from March tenth through the seventeenth, please."

"Yah mon, yah know dat's no problem. Ask for Miss Lena when yah get here den."

"Wait, don't hang up," I said. "Don't you need a credit card number to hold the room?"

"What ya talkin' bout mon? Ya never been to Jamaica before, have you? The reservation is in my head. Your name is Robert and you'll be here the tenth yeah?"

"Uh, uh, um, yeah, the tenth."

That was an awfully long way to fly without a reservation, I worried.

"The rooms are fifteen a night, and I'll see you on the tenth," said the charming Miss Lena while she practically hung up the phone.

"Mom, the good news is that we got a cabin for the week. The scary news is that she didn't ask me for any credit card to hold the room. No driver's license, nothing. We're going a long, long, ways and all we can do is ask for Miss Lena. Do you think there's more than one Miss Lena in Jamaica?" I laughed.

The month that we had to wait seemed to take forever. I was working a lot and so was Marianne. I tried my best to stay out of her and Ken's way around the house so they would have some privacy. I kept to myself in my room a lot. But every night that I was home, she would knock on the door and come in to tell me goodnight. She even tucked me into bed once in a while. She'd giggle and say, "Does my baby boy need to be tucked in?" She cracked me up, but I actually did like it when she tucked me in. We had known each other for a little over a year and in ways I must have seemed like a baby to her. I was the biggest one-year-old she had ever seen.

She would sit on the edge of the bed and just look at me so tenderly. I was really becoming close with Marianne, just the way I had hoped. There was just one thing that we couldn't talk about, and we talked about everything and anything. I even told her about my sex life like I would a close friend. But the subject that stopped us in our tracks and threatened to make her cry every time, was my father.

It had been quite a long time since the last time I brought it up because it had made her cry and I couldn't bear seeing that. She had told me enough that I could begin to make a rudimentary search for him. The problem was that she wasn't certain of the spelling of his last name. It was very French, and she thought it was spelled, "deRossier." She also thought he would probably be in Canada or Paris. So blindly I started dialing phone numbers in Montreal and asking for 'Guy deRossier.' There were about fifteen of them in the directory and the operator was kind enough to give me all fifteen numbers. One by one I dialed them and checked them off. The conversations were brief and awkward. "Hello, did you have a son that was given up for adoption in 1963?" I got everything from hang-ups, to people who only spoke French, and some who were angry. I quit after going through the list. I knew intuitively that this was not the way. It was a needle in a monstrous haystack. I got much closer when I called a record store in Vancouver, B. C. and asked if they had any records by an artist named Guy deRossier. One of the owners was certain that he recognized the name but informed me he didn't have any of the records in stock nor did he know how to get them. The difficulty was compounded by the fact that we couldn't be certain of the spelling of his last name.

Back on the edge of my bed, Marianne's eyes got that misty look as I again asked her to tell me about my father.

"I wish I knew how to find him for you Robert, I just don't know where to begin. All I can tell you is that if you look at yourself in the mirror, you'll find him there. You look a lot like him."

"Thanks, Mom, I don't mean to upset you. And as long as I've got you, that's all that matters."

"Yes Robert, but you need to know your father too. Someday, somehow, I know you will."

She tucked me in and kissed me on the forehead. When the door closed I vowed never to bring him up again. It only served to upset Marianne, and I couldn't bear to see that one more time. I was content with her anyway.

"Mom, am I the youngest looking thirty-year-old you've ever seen or what?"

"It's those big eyes and baby face of yours, Robert."

I wasn't actually thirty yet but I would be in a few days. I was packing my suitcase for our trip to Jamaica. Marianne started packing about a week ahead of time. We were leaving that night, and I had just started packing. But then, I was used to living out of a suitcase.

I routed us on a non-stop red-eye from Seattle to Miami. It would put us into Miami first thing in the morning. We'd then have to connect from Miami to Montego Bay. We'd be on the beach the following afternoon.

The five-hour flight through the night would have been more tolerable if my knees weren't under my chin. But I somehow managed to sleep a bit on Marianne's shoulder. We were both so anxious to be on the beach. We were so tight. She had become my best friend. Someone on the flight mentioned something to us about a honeymoon. I was half asleep until Marianne woke me up laughing.

"No, no," she said." This is my son, we're not going on a honeymoon."

She turned red to match her hair. I laughed.

"See how fine you look, Momma," I said in my best Otis alter ego voice.

We got off of the plane in Miami and the air smelled different. Warmer. Sultry. I liked it. I knew airports like the back of my hand and told Marianne to follow me. A very odd thing happened as we walked through the Miami airport. I started seeing all kinds of people who resembled me. Everywhere I looked. I didn't recall once ever being startled by a resemblance in Seattle. Not even close.

"I like Miami, Mom," I turned to Marianne and said.

"You like the girls," she laughed.

"Well, that too," I confessed.

As we passed through the electronic checkpoint, two girls looked at me then started speaking Spanish. They must have heard me speaking English to Marianne and assumed I didn't know Spanish. But I had been Spanish language-qualified to fly trips to Mexico for Alaska Airlines. I wasn't fluent, but I knew enough to know exactly what they were saying. They said, "*Que bonitos ojos azules tienes* The dialect was not Mexican. It sounded South American, and they looked like they were Brazilian or Argentinean. I freaked them out when I walked over and said in Spanish, "*Muchas gracias, sus ojos son bonitas tambien.*" I thanked them and told them they had pretty eyes too. They nearly choked.

"See Momma, I like this place. I feel home here." I added, "The Norwegian girls in Seattle just do not give me any kind of attention."

We continued down the long terminal where we noticed that many of the airport laborers looked unique. They were black, but without the typical North American black features.

"I wonder if they're Haitian, Mom?"

"Look at the high cheek bones," she agreed.

We continued through the airport until we came to our gate. We had five hours to kill before our flight into Montego Bay, so we set up a little camp near a concession area. I pulled two chairs together so that I could go to sleep. I was still very tired. Marianne went to look for a smoking area.

I may have been out for hours when Marianne poked me in the ribs.

"Robert, wake up. There's a lady right over there who has been walking back and forth staring at you."

"What are you talking about, Mom?" I said as I wiped my eyes.

"I think maybe she likes you," Marianne giggled in her little schoolgirl way. "I wonder if she's Jamaican?"

"Ask her," I said.

Marianne was ten times more outgoing than I was. If it were me, I wouldn't have asked. But in her pure, innocent way she just blurted out, "Are you Jamaican?"

"No, I'm Haitian," the woman said, taking a few steps closer to us.

That got my attention. I was still waking up, but I sat straight up in my chair now. She continued staring at me in a familiar way, pondering just how it was that she knew me. It was a little eerie, actually.

"My father is Haitian too."

The woman looked through me like she was trying to identify a picture in her photo album she hadn't seen in years.

"Who is your father?" she asked.

"His name is Guy deRossier."

That moment she sprang to life and became extremely animated.

"I knew it. You look just like Guy duRosier."

"Are you talking about Guy duRosier, the entertainer?" Marianne said as she scooted up to the edge of her seat in attention.

"Of course!" the Haitian stranger replied emphatically.

Marianne and I looked at each other tensely, in disbelief.

"I have never met my father. I was adopted as an infant, and I just met my mom last year."

This mysterious woman moved in closer so that she was now about five feet from us.

"How could you not know Guy duRosier? Every Haitian knows him. Three generations listen to his music. I just saw him live in concert here in Miami two weeks ago."

Marianne was shaking. Literally shaking. She steadied herself by squeezing my hand.

"Oh my god Robert. This is unbelievable. I have to have a smoke before I pass out."

"My name is Robert duRosier," I said intensely to this stranger in the airport. "I have never even seen a photograph of my father. Nothing. Is there anything you can do to help me find him?"

"I'm on your case," she said.

Just like that. I didn't even know her name yet. Marianne asked her, and she said that her name was Ethel St. Claire. I thought to myself, *"Saint is quite an appropriate surname for this woman."*

Marianne exchanged phone numbers and addresses with Ethel St. Claire. I was in a trance.

"You need to know your father, and I'm on your case," Ethel St. Claire said to me.

She said it so matter of fact, like she was an attorney handling a case.

My spine tingled because my spirituality recognized this was something unexplainable. Maybe Ethel St. Claire was God's attorney, and if so, she could handle my case any day. Marianne and I sat in a lucid silence for a moment. We looked at each other to make sure it wasn't a dream. We were both completely freaked out. There was no other way to put it.

"Mom, was that an angel?" I asked. I added before she could respond, "Did you touch her at all to make sure she was real?"

I wasn't kidding.

"Robert, I just can't believe it," Marianne stammered as she held her hands over her mouth.

I wondered what in the world it was about me and airports. I was having some incredible things happen to me in airports. We had practically forgotten about our trip to Jamaica when we heard the gate agents make the first boarding call.

The view out of the passenger side window was spectacular. The sea was aquamarine and there was not a cloud in the sky. I took a moment to reflect as I gazed out the window. Twenty-four years ago I had been a little boy standing in Ivo Bannister's garage hearing that my father was a Tahitian sailor. Now it seemed so long ago. Ethel St. Claire's stirring words echoed in my mind. "Do you realize that when your father performs live, the ambulances arrive early in anticipation of all of the fainting victims? Your father is the most charismatic singer Haiti has ever known." And she certainly treated me like royalty in that airport. She all but asked me for my autograph. A sailor. I scoffed at the idea. I also recalled the times when, on occasion people would tell me they wished they were adopted. They'd say, "Don't feel so bad that you were adopted, the way my parents treat me, I wish I were too." It was really uncanny how many times I heard that twisted attempt at logic. I didn't care how demented somebody's parents were. To at least see where you've come from is fundamental to one's development. I felt like slapping people who said that to me. I think my anger could be attributed, at that moment, to the fact that I suddenly knew my father was alive and out in the world someplace. And that he was an artist, just as I should have been all along. It's how my DNA was coded. I wasn't meant to take engines apart and work on cars every day. I was looking for my place in the world, and I never seemed to quite fit into any slot I chose. *'I wish I were adopted too,' my ass*, I said to myself.

The plane landed perfectly onto the tarmac at Montego Bay and we quickly shuttled through customs and found ourselves outside, negotiating taxi fare to Negril. Marianne and I were so thrilled, we could barely contain ourselves. I felt a little foolish when one of the drivers asked me where I was staying.

"Mom if I tell him 'Ozzie's Shack,' is he going to laugh at me?"

She laughed nervously and waited for me to make a fool out of myself.

"We're staying at 'Ozzie's Shack' in Negril. Do you have any idea where that is?" I asked.

"Oh yah mon. You and your mom gwine to go see Miss Lena, den," said the driver.

That was the magic name I was looking to hear. I felt a bit relieved, as we at the very least would make it to our destination. What happened when we arrived was still uncertain.

All we could do was cross our fingers and hope she had saved us a place.

The van ride was long. It was over an hour and a half to Negril. All along the way we saw little schoolchildren wearing blue uniforms and walking single file on the sides of the streets. We also saw men continuously selling marijuana. They would even chase after the van and put it in the windows for us to smell. Crazy looking Rastafarians with blood-red eyes would holler, "Dis here da best ghanja in Jamaica mon. You buy, mon." Somebody else in our van bought some and a big group of girls lit some up. *What a country*, I laughed to myself.

By the time we arrived in Negril, I was feeling funny just from the smoke in the van. The driver called out to us that we had arrived at Ozzie's. When I paid him the taxi fare I looked at Marianne and laughed, "Mom, do you realize that cab ride cost more than our flight?" She looked right through me with glazed-over eyes. She was high. I thought it was hilarious. I may have been a bit as well. We walked through a grassy pathway back towards the beach. Just as the cabins came into view, I spotted a really large woman underneath a palm tree, just sitting there shading herself.

"Must be Robert and Marianne dere," she smiled.

She hollered at two girls with brooms and motioned for them to go clean out the cabin near the shore. It was spectacular. It looked like something straight out of a Hemingway novel. The cabins were painted a rust color and were offset by beautiful lime green queen palms, the likes of which I'd never seen. They didn't grow that way in Arizona or California. And, no more than thirty yards from the steps of our cabin, there lay the Caribbean. It was impossibly blue-green, or teal in color. I dropped my suitcase and gave the red head a hug.

"Now this is what I'm talkin' about, Momma."

One of the guys sitting out on his porch with his feet outstretched remarked, "Is this your honeymoon?" It happened again. I couldn't believe it.

"This is my mother, Marianne. And my name is Robert."

He couldn't believe Marianne was my mother, and she liked it.

We walked in the cabin and put our things away. I sat down at the foot of my bed and Marianne did the same. We looked across the room at each other.

"Robert, your father is out there somewhere. I just know you're going to find him now," Marianne reminded me.

"God Mom, wouldn't that be great. Do you think she'll really find him?"

"Well, she said she was on your case. I believe her."

We arrived just in time to see what had become quite a tradition in Negril. Everyone flocked to the beach to watch the magnificent sunsets there. We could've seen it right from our front porch, but we decided to walk down to the beach and people- watch too. Out on the horizon a huge burnt- orange ball was dropping right into the sea. There was not one cloud in the sky. It was spectacular. Breathtaking.

"Mom, it feels like I'm having prayers that have been in the balance for thirty years answered all at once. My head is spinning," I said.

"I know. What happened today was just a miracle. It really was," she said.

"Did you see the way she talked about him?" I said.

She gave me a mischievous look.

"Your father was something else, I told you. You're going to meet him, I just know it."

The week flew by on the beach. I spent all day long out on a raft on the water just soaking up the sun. I had my color back. The Jamaicans had taken to calling me 'Superstar'. It turns out that is an affectionate term they use for people mixed with black and white. The nickname originated with their reggae superstar, Bob Marley. I befriended one

Jamaican in particular named Tony. His nickname was 'Blacks,' because he was as black as black gets. Tony would lie in a hammock in the shade all day long and talk with Marianne and me. He was always smoking ganja too. In the afternoons, we'd see him come strolling up to the cabin with his machete in one hand and several stalks of sugar cane in the other. He'd split the cane expertly while we looked on. That sugar cane was like a sweet rush to the senses. It was delicious. Then Tony would put some reggae music on while we relaxed and sang along waiting for the sunset. The days were easy in Jamaica. One afternoon I asked Tony where he got the large scars on his stomach.

"Tony, what happened there?" I pointed.

"Oh Superstar, one ting yah muss know 'bout Jamaica mon, nobody fights with him fist here. Broken glass is always in a fight mon. So one day, dis rude boy come upon me talkin' nonsense and him cut me. Me did nottin to him mon. Me tanks Jah every day dat I'm still livin. Now nobody vex me no more Robert."

"Yeah Blacks, you are way too mellow for anybody to mess with," I said.

We laughed and let the trade winds blow through our hammocks. Tony was close with Marianne too. In fact he had progressed to the point where he was calling her Mom. I thought it was great. I would have liked to bring Tony home with us if I could. He used to love to drink Guinness beer. He said it was good for 'the bamboo.' I'd joke with him and tell him, "Tony, that motor oil you call beer might be good for a car, but not for 'the big bamboo'." He'd laugh and all you could see were his teeth brightening up the night sky. He wasn't nicknamed "Blacks," for nothing.

"Hey Superstar, I'm original black mon. No slave owners have mixed him blood in Black's family."

When it came time to leave, Tony was visibly upset. We had become as close as brothers, and he was like a son to Marianne as well. He actually cried the night before we had to leave. I told him I would come back to this paradise for sure. Maybe even within a year. I meant it too. That place was like Nirvana or something.

I went to settle our bill with Miss Lena and was astonished at the small amount we had to part with to pay the bill. It was a steal.

"Mom, we did this trip the right way. We stayed around the local Jamaican people and hung out with them. That's what I call culture.

We could have stayed in a nice hotel and not had any interaction with the people, but we did it right."

She, like Tony, was saddened to have to leave.

"Yeah we did, Robert. I don't want to leave."

The taxi ride back to Montego Bay was agonizing. Watching the white sand disappear and the teal water fade from our sight was terrible. But I did have one big thing to look forward to. I was hoping to hear from Ethel St. Claire in a few weeks. I figured I'd give her a few weeks, and if I didn't hear from her then I would call her.

The air was absolutely frigid when we arrived back home. The cold air actually almost hurt me.

"Ouch," I yelled to Marianne.

We got out of the car and I grabbed both of our suitcases to drag them into the house. It was late, so I was sure to be quiet so as not to wake up Ken. Marianne went to check the mailbox. I was already inside the house putting my suitcase away when I heard a loud whisper.

"Robert, come here quick." Marianne's eyes were excited and she was smiling at me oddly.

"What's up, Mom?" I asked.

She held up a Federal Express package.

"You've got mail from Ethel St. Claire," she beamed.

Everything around me slowed down as I tore through that package like my life depended on how quickly I could rip it open.

Inside there appeared to be something large like a record album. I turned it upside down and out slid two records.

"There's your father Robert, oh my god, it's him on the cover!" Marianne gasped, putting her hands on both of her cheeks in awe.

I was in shock. I was numb. I was thrilled. It was like looking in the mirror. Then we saw the other record. Again there was a photo of him on the cover and back.

"Your father was probably your age in this photo."

She held her hand up over her mouth while I stared and stared at those records. Then I finally found the letter that Ethel sent with the package. It said, "Dear Robert and Marianne, I went to 'Little Haiti,' in Miami and asked everybody about your father, Guy. It took a couple of days but I found someone who knows him. So here is his address and phone number in Haiti and in the Bahamas where he's currently living. He has many more records but I could only send these two for now."

"Mom, how did we go from not being sure how to spell his name, to having pictures, addresses, and phone numbers in the last two weeks?"

"It's a miracle, Robert." She added, "I want to listen to those records but we can't wake Ken. We'll listen tomorrow, okay?"

I got into bed and held onto both records. I stared at them and tried to make out the text, but it was all in French. I studied every line in his face. I couldn't take my eyes off of him, but I was so tired from the long flight that I finally fell asleep. When I woke the following morning, I had my arms wrapped around both records tightly. I was like a little kid. I opened my eyes slowly, hoping that it all wasn't just some great dream. My eyes came into focus and there was my father, Guy duRosier, again. I examined the spelling of his last name on the record. I did indeed have the spelling wrong during all of those fruitless phone calls I had made to Montreal.

I realized quickly that morning that I was a phone call away from speaking to him, and that made me very nervous. That would not be the way to go about this, however. I didn't want to shock him or scare him. So I decided to sit down and write a long letter to him explaining how we had located him. I would enclose a photograph of Marianne from 1962 and a recent photograph of myself, so that he would know it wasn't some kind of a hoax. I explained to him that I didn't want anything from him other than to just meet him and shake his hand. I asked Marianne to read the letter and give it her approval. She did. And off it went into the mailbox. My heart and soul was packaged up inside of a little envelope and on its way to Nassau, Bahamas. I hoped and prayed like never before that it would come back to me intact.

Part III

THE PHILOSOPHER'S STONE

"By honors, medals, titles no true man is elated. To realize that which we are, this is the honor for which we are created."

ANGELUS SILISEOUS

7

DESTINY

Day after day I went to the mailbox only to find nothing. When I flew, I called Marianne from my layover as soon as I arrived at the hotel to ask if I'd received anything in the mail. The answer was repeatedly no. It had been over a month now since I sent my father that letter. I was edgy. I had to get my mind around the possibility that he just might blow me off completely. That was not pleasant. I remained optimistic, albeit very guardedly optimistic.

One day, Marianne walked over and sat down beside me.

"Robert, don't worry. He will write back. He's just got to. He's not the kind of man who would do anything less. I know that much about him."

"Thanks Mom, that helps. You always know how to make me feel better."

Life had become mundane again after the natural letdown from Jamaica. I continued to fly extra trips when I could and working was easy because it was the only thing that could take my mind off my anxiety over my father. I thought of a thousand possible scenarios to explain the delay in correspondence. *Maybe he's no longer in the Bahamas,* I suggested to myself. If that were true, he probably never got my letter. That was a distinct possibility. Or maybe the mail just took a long time to process from the Caribbean. I tricked myself into every conceivable excuse to retain some sanity.

It was already the third week of April and still no word. On one of my rare days off from flying, I sat impatiently waiting for the mailman to stop by before I left to run some errands. He was there at his usual eleven a. m. The mail looked different as I reached in and pulled out a manila envelope with 'Air Mail' stamped all over it. Then I noticed 'Express Delivery' stamped as well. As my eyes moved to the upper right corner I saw four colorful stamps and they all said 'Bahamas' on them. I got it! The letter from my father that I had been waiting and praying for. There it was in my hands! I studied the way he wrote his name in the inside address. I ran inside the house and called Marianne at work to tell her about it.

"Mom, it's here. The letter from Guy!"

"Oh goody. What did he say?"

"Well, I haven't even opened it up yet," I answered.

"Call me back after you read it Robert. Oh, I'm so thrilled for you."

I hung up the phone and paced around the house with the letter in my hand. I was afraid to open it. I finally had what I wanted so badly, and now I was deathly afraid of what the contents may contain. I was home alone; still, I locked myself in the bathroom and sat staring at the letter. After a few minutes I finally found my courage and I tore into that letter. What I read that day was one of the most magnificent pieces of writing I've ever seen. I was awed by it.

The letter read as follows:

My Beloved Son,

The wonderful news concerning your mother and yourself being alive and well has had a wonderful effect on my metabolism…for, rest assured, my romance with your mother never had the shape of a summer affair; no, we were deeply in love, and when she became pregnant, that love degenerated into passion at the hands of racists. I was far from thinking that I would never, ever see her again, nor hear from her. Imagine a moment that a woman tells you about expecting a child with you, and then she vanishes, disappears from your view for three decades.

Nopson, (I refuse to call him mister), was the vector of this tragedy. Your mother was martyred and left to accept all of the pain.

Racism is a very weak word to describe what has happened; I call it Hitlerism, chauvinism, an excessive worship of one's self, and the Arian race, belliguous, xenophobe, hostile to anything foreign and so on and so forth.

Three good people, three innocent creatures have paid a high price for that "anti-Christ" attitude. There is great disappointment over

Nopson's attitude, on the other hand, since April first, a tremendous joy has invaded my heart and soul. I have at last recuperated my son, that I love. I am overwhelmed, and should stop crying and complaining.

Your mother says in the letter that you resemble me; I have never dreamed of being so handsome and candid – you are Guy and Marianne combined, conceived in a beautiful summer 1962.

After the sublime reunification of father, mother, and son could I call you an alchemist? I am certain that you are since you took the ashes of our hearts and converted them into the "philosophical stone," "la pierre philosophade."

You have a poetical and lyrical pen that has recomposed me. I tend to sometimes translate from French into English and commit some errors. So I apologize for the word 'lyrical pen,' to describe your erudition. I didn't want to go through an intellectual thesis, or talk about division or subdivision of logics; I only know about dividing harmony. Within any good writer there is a great grammarian with the gift of style, and an undeniable authenticity that conforms to the truth without ornament. Yes, Robert, my prince, progress was made since the generation has embettered itself. I am very, very proud.

Thank you for coming back to me. Marianne and I were brutally separated because of epidermical prejudice (I don't know how much consideration people give to the ink of spirit; after all, racism has no scientific basis).

Your mother is extremely exquisite and your father is no blue-collar, so you know by now who you are.

If you are still in touch with the Bannisters, please tell them that your biological father will never forget them in his prayers.

Please Robert, make sure that you'll never lose me again. Watch over and protect your mother. I'll call you on the 25th of April and then we'll arrange a meeting place somewhere…however, I wouldn't wish that meeting to take place anywhere near the Nopson's. Your mother is the only Nopson that I care for.

I am enchanted,

Love, Father Guy

I was stunned when I finished the letter. Never had I seen such expressive, colorful writing. It was hypnotic. For the first time in this journey of mine, I became aware that my quest was taking on a life of its own. There were other people as affected as I was. I had never stopped to think of the impact on both Guy and Marianne. I simply knew that I needed my mother and father. However, after reading his letter, I knew that the scope of this saga was going to get larger and larger.

When I re-read Guy's letter I was astonished that he had received my letter on April 1st. If Guy had been an American and observed our holidays, he would have considered that letter to be the worst April Fool's day prank imaginable! "*Thank God the Haitians don't have an April Fool's day*," I thought.

Three things were quite obvious to me from his letter. First, my father was extremely proud to be black. He attacked racism zealously.

Second, he was very intelligent. The letter was so very literate and philosophical. I was intimidated by it, in some respects. And last, he loved me and wanted to develop some relationship. That's all I was asking for.

After corresponding a few more times through the mail, we agreed that I would phone him on Sunday. I picked up the telephone and dialed his phone number in Nassau, Bahamas. After four long rings, he picked up the receiver. He had a soft, quiet tone.

"Hello, Guy, this is Robert."

"Thanks be to God, my son."

He repeated my name three times. And he said 'Robert,' but he said it in French so that it sounded like, "Robaire." I thought it sounded quite dignified. He had a very thick French accent. In fact, his English was a little difficult to understand. On one of the records that Ethel St. Claire had sent me was a song called "Papa," that his daughter, D'Jenane had sung. It was so cute. She sounded like she was maybe seven or eight years old at the time.

"Guy, would you mind if I called you Papa, like D'Jenane does in that song?" I asked.

"Of course Robaire, I would be honored. I am your papa after all."

"Would you like me to fly to Nassau so that we can meet face-to-face?" I asked.

"I would like you to come here, but I am going to Haiti for two concerts and I will be there most all of June. I would invite you to Haiti, but the political climate is very volatile right now. A coup is inevitable and I would not advise you to be there during this time. But can you come to Nassau in the first week of July?"

"Yeah, no problem at all. I will plan on it," I said.

"This will give us another month to get to know one another via written correspondence and Sunday phone calls," Guy added.

He was patient. So was I. I could wait. But I would have preferred to go to Haiti regardless of the political climate. Later, I would come to understand more about that mysterious little island, Haiti, and be happy that I didn't travel there in June.

"Robaire, you have a beautiful sister in Ecuador. D'Jenane is studying drama there. She was born in Ecuador while I was living there and doing film scoring. You will meet her soon."

"Papa, I can't wait to see you and shake your hand."

Just then, Marianne walked into the room and asked me for the phone. I handed her the phone and she said, "Guy, hello, this is Marianne."

I was staring at my mother, who was talking to my father. How thrilling that was!

"Yes," she agreed, "It has been a long, long time." She added, "Yes, he is handsome. He looks a lot like you."

She was always so flattering with me. I began to see things so clearly that moment. I knew that if we are to live life in harmony with the universe, we must possess a powerful faith in what the ancients used to call "fatem," what we currently refer to as "destiny." I clung to the theory that life is not a series of meaningless accidents or coincidences, but rather it is a tapestry of events that culminate in an exquisite, sublime, plan. That giant ball that I had begun pushing up hill, back on that bleak day in Phoenix, was now gaining enough momentum to begin rolling on its own and it was at the crest of a steep hill ready to pummel anything in its path.

I watched Marianne curiously as she spoke to Guy. She had that twinkle in her eyes that gives her away every time. She only got that look when she was very excited. It made me happy to see her happy. Beyond that, my intuitive nature, in which I placed a great deal of faith, sensed something brewing.

I routed my trip almost the same as our Jamaica trip. The red-eye non-stop to Miami, then I would take a commuter flight to Nassau, Bahamas, arriving the following afternoon at one.

"Robert, you have to promise to call me when you get there," Marianne demanded.

"Don't worry Redhead, I'll call."

"I am so jealous, I want to go too," she said.

"I don't think Ken would like that much, Momma." I warned her.

"I know. Darn," she said as frustrated as I had ever seen her.

"You tell Guy that Marianne says hello."

"I will, Mom. I love you."

I was off. It was like, 'here we go again.' The emotional courage it takes to put oneself out there hoping that a stranger will accept and love them is remarkable. I had gone through the fire once and was about to do it again. I was far more nervous about this trip, however. I rationalized that it should be part of a mother's nature to be loving and nurturing. I half-expected what I got from Marianne. This man waiting for me in the Caribbean was far more of a mystery to me. But it was all I knew how to do. I was going after my people. I was on a hero's journey, and I did it with reckless, blind faith because I had nothing to lose. I was doing the only thing I could do. Taking action. I boarded the commuter flight on the tarmac in Miami. It was a little propeller plane that seated twelve passengers. I was an hour away from meeting my father. I shook along with the plane the whole way there.

8

NON-ANTICIPATION

Tʀᴜᴇ rewards come when effort is put forth with no thought of gain. It is also when one is behaving most naturally and spontaneously close to their nature. To strive for power or gifts is to become lost in lust. It's when we sit down with no thought of results that results come the fastest. It is a paradox. Yet, it is admittedly the way I chose to behave in my pursuit of my father. And it helped calm me down on the short flight to Nassau. I wasn't expecting anything of him. I simply wanted to shake his hand and look him in the eye. After that, I would let things take their natural course.

I carefully negotiated the four steps off of the little commuter plane. When I hit the bottom, I immediately looked up to see if he was there. The problem was, there were no people allowed to greet the passengers. They were held in the baggage claim area. So I had to delay my gratification momentarily. I paced through the Nassau airport, small as it was, until I came to the baggage claim. I collected my things and still did not see Guy. Next, I walked with my suitcase out of the airport doors to the sidewalk where taxis and other people were waiting. Just then, he came walking towards me, from across the street. It was me in another thirty years! The shoulders, the stride, the shape of his head were all mine. The same blueprint indeed. He got closer and I saw his eyes. They were different. They were huge. He had big, round, expressive eyes and he looked nervous. He grinned at me as we shook hands, and then he reached out to carry my suitcase for me. I slowed him down and said, "Hi, Papa."

"God is surely rubbing his hands together pleased with what he has done," he said as he raised outstretched arms to the sky. The imagery created by his speech was just as magnificent as his letters.

"*Bon dieu, bon dieu,*" he cried over and over again.

As we drove alongside the beautiful ocean on our way to the Buena Vista resort, Guy said, "Robaire, if I had known I only had to take the stage in Miami in order to recover you, I would have come out of retirement long ago." He equated Ethel St. Claire's attendance at his Miami concert with her being able to put us together. And he was right.

"India messed me up. I was in Bombay performing under contract with the Sheraton Hotel and everyone lives like a monk there. So I quit performing live and had been living like a dead man for a few years here in Nassau. That Miami concert was my first live gig in a few years."

I didn't say much. I was busy studying his interesting face. I was like an art student at the Louvre in Paris. I was entranced. He was black, but he did not look like the typical black American. And he had the hands of a giant. They were like a seven-foot man's hands, massive. I had never before felt my hand swallowed up in anyone's hand like that. I had on a short sleeve shirt, as did Guy. He moved his arm over beside my forearm to compare and they were identical in every respect. He shook his head back and forth, mystified.

"My progeny," he declared.

I figured at this pace, I was going to have to keep a dictionary with me around him. He spoke a very sophisticated English. I could only imagine how his French must be if he spoke English at the level he did.

Then he looked at me earnestly and said, "You are my hero!" I felt odd. I was doing the only thing I knew to do. And my father just called me his hero. I felt so happy that I could have cried. I felt appreciated for who and what I was for the first time. Validated by the one person from whom it meant the most, my father.

We checked into the Buena Vista Hotel, where he was performing a few nights a week. We talked for about an hour and began to get to know each other. Then he said he would be back later that evening to perform and invited me to come downstairs for dinner and his show.

"Robaire, you can eat whatever you like, everything is on the house for you this week," he said. He added, "This is Nassau's finest restaurant so you will see a five star menu."

"Okay Papa, I'll see you a little bit later."

I slept very hard that afternoon. And when I woke about four hours later, it was to the sound of a piano and my father's voice. He was singing a beautiful ballad in what I thought was Italian. I thought to myself, *"He didn't come and wake me up. Just like I would have done."* He was always concerned with etiquette. He probably would have deliberated for over an hour about whether it was polite or not to wake me. Our personalities were very similar. Everything about him was subtle, except his voice. That was a booming, thunderous, tenor the likes of which I had only heard from the famous tenors, Pavarotti, Domingo, and Carreras. At the end of the song a rousing round of applause wafted up the staircase and down the hallway towards my room. I sat straight up in my bed, the room now completely darkened. I thought I was dreaming the music at first, and then I realized it was Guy downstairs. I hurried into the shower not wanting to miss another second of his show.

I put on a jacket and tie and hurried down the beautiful spiral staircase that led to the formal dining room. I paused to look up at the large crystal chandelier at the bottom of the stairs. The maitre de was an impressive looking man. His skin, black like charcoal, had a dignified sheen. He spoke very proper English the way the Bahamian people did. 'The King's English,' they called it. "Right this way Mr. duRosier," he said to me. The sound of it was like music to my ears. Papa must have told him to be expecting me. And the fact that he called me 'duRosier' didn't escape me either. The room was spectacular. Everywhere I looked there were chandeliers and crystal. The wait staff was dressed in black pants and red tuxedo coats. The service was impeccable to the point that I had to be careful not to embarrass myself and to be sure of my manners. Guy winked at me from the piano as he elegantly made his way through a lovely ballad that I could not identify. Seated at the long table beside me was a group of Italians. They were all dressed beautifully. They were chatting amongst themselves, when suddenly they all turned their attention toward Guy in surprise. They all stopped talking simultaneously as he began to forcefully turn the room on its ear with a tenor so rich that it brought to mind Luciano Pavarotti. And his Italian was perfect. I didn't speak Italian, but I knew what the accent sounded like. They were flabbergasted to see this black man in the Bahamas singing like one of their beloved countrymen. After the song was finished, Guy received a stirring round of applause from the room, especially from the group beside me. Two of the men approached the piano and began speaking with Guy in Italian. I was amazed that this was my father. *"Who exactly is this guy?"*

I wondered. They took photographs with him. Guy was not through blowing my mind yet. His next number was completely different. He played a magnificent Brazilian samba. It got my shoulders rolling and my feet tapping. What a piano player, and moreover, what a singer! Guy motioned me over to the piano on his next break. "Robaire, do you see your father is a polyglot?" he asked.

I smiled and nodded my head, not having any idea what he meant. I pretended to know what polyglot meant, but the first chance I got away from him I looked up the word and found the answer. 'A person having a speaking, reading, or writing knowledge of several languages.' He was certainly that.

"Did you order your dinner yet?" he asked.

"Yes, I ordered the filet mignon."

After he finished up his last set, Guy came over to my table and joined me for dinner. I was amazed by him but he was very quiet, very humble away from the stage. He spoke very softly. We talked about music. I told him that jazz was my favorite form of music. He was proud of that.

"In that case, tomorrow I have a gig at a jazz club where I'll play my 'axe' for a couple of sets," he said.

He liked to call his saxophone, his axe.

"You mean to tell me you play the sax, Papa?"

"Yes Robaire, it is my most proficient instrument. I studied under Dr. Billy Taylor, and Bud Johnson at the Berklee College of Music in Boston."

I owned CDs by both of those artists. And I understood Berklee to be one of the two best music schools in the world, along with Julliard.

"You're too much, Papa," something I would grow accustomed to saying quite often.

He introduced me to the entire staff of the Buena Vista, then we went upstairs to crash for the night. We had a big suite with two large beds and we each stretched our long legs out and couldn't sleep a wink. We talked almost all night. I told Guy all about my childhood. At times he winced as his face became noticeably beleaguered with pain. Any time he heard the word 'adopted' or 'orphanage', he hid his face in the palm of his huge hand, then just shook his head back and forth.

"Robaire, you are a big, strong man, yet you have the heart of a woman."

I was amazed at how quickly he had sized me up. He was right but nobody had ever put it in those words to me before. I felt exposed.

"That is the highest compliment a man could receive. I am just like you. To be physically imposing yet spiritually gentle, is to be perfectly balanced," he said, easing my obvious confusion. I felt like I was listening to a guru. In a sense, he was. He always gave me the impression that he was more spirit than matter.

"Papa," I said, "I have to ask you something important that I've been thinking about all evening."

He raised his head quickly as if to say, "Go ahead."

"Would you mind if I were to take your last name?"

He rolled over on his side and moaned in laughter that gave away his joy with the question.

"Ah Robaire, duRosier *is* your name, my prince. You were only renting the name Bannister."

He had made me feel better about myself in one day than I had my entire youth. He had called me his hero, his prince, and he understood that I have the heart of a woman. I was him. I was just, incredibly like him. Our birthdays were both in March, too.

"Thanks, Papa, I will represent the name well," I smiled.

"Alleluia, and excelsior," he exclaimed. He finally mentioned that we must get some sleep.

"Remind me to call Marianne tomorrow, Papa."

"Oh yes, the little girl."

He said it very affectionately. I grinned off to sleep. It was July 6th, 1993, and I was thirty years, three months, and twenty days old. It was the first evening that I slept comfortably knowing who I was and where I was from. It was the first evening I ever experienced a truly sound, gratifying, restful sleep.

When I woke, Guy was already awake, staring at me from across the room.

"Robaire, do you realize you were laughing in your sleep?"

"I was?" I asked.

"A man must have not a care in the world to accomplish laughter in his sleep, Robaire!" We both laughed hard.

We got in his car and drove towards his house that morning so that I could see where he lived and we could call Marianne. It was a small house that he was renting a room in, and he was indeed living like a monk. It was a mess. He was like the classic artist who is extremely structured when it comes to his art, and a complete mess otherwise. "You know that my mother, your grandmother, Mama Francine calls me Beethoven, Robaire?" I could see why. He was practically helpless outside of his music. I wouldn't have been surprised to find his socks in the freezer.

I got Marianne on the phone and told her what a great time I was having. Guy was standing outside with me on the porch, practicing his golf swing in the sun. Marianne was very jealous of me for being in the Caribbean. Guy whispered a request to speak to Marianne for a moment. I handed him the phone and he started talking with her like they had never been apart. He called her 'Cherie,' and 'Darling,' so affectionately that it made me wonder what she was saying back. I was curious but I gave him his privacy. He looked thrilled to be speaking with her, especially with his son by his side. He raved about me to her. It was hard to act like a grown man when inside I felt like a little kid. I had to subdue my pure joy all of the time around my father. Guy handed the phone back to me and I listened to Marianne's sweet voice declare, "Robert, I wish I were there with you and your father." I let the slightest hint of hope captivate me at that moment. The hope that somehow, someway, they might be together. I knew that look that Marianne had in her eyes when she saw the album cover with Guy on it. Those twinkling eyes said more than a thousand words could have. And here I was, outside in the sun in the Bahamas, witnessing a similar display of rapture on the face of my father. *"But no, no, no, it's just not possible,"* I chastised myself.

That day we drove back to the Buena Vista where Guy sat me down at the piano with him and asked me if he could test my vocal range. The prior evening during our marathon conversation I told him all about my years in choir at the Catholic school, and how I tried to play the saxophone. I piqued his curiosity indeed as he ran through some scales and asked me to follow him.

"Robaire, you are a singer! We will record together soon," he said, satisfied.

"Yeah Papa, that sounds like a lot of fun."

"But you will have to learn to sing in Creole and French."

I didn't really think he was serious, but the thought of it alone was enough to get excited over. Guy said, "The way you sing, your tone, and your lack of vibrato, is reminiscent of the great Brazilian singers. You remind me Gilberto Gil, or Milton Nascimento." He was blowing my mind. I figured I was nothing more than a shower singer who grew up listening to Earth Wind and Fire, Marvin Gaye, Stevie Wonder, and the great Motown artists. But Guy had my mind spinning with the possibilities he was presenting.

Nighttime was spectacular in Nassau. We drove along the shoreline and witnessed the stars just beginning to twinkle above the azure-colored sea. The air was sultry. Humid, yet not too hot. Guy was dressed now more casually in a white guayabera and brown pants. The shirt contrasted with his beautiful skin color. It was like dark caramel. My father was handsome indeed. He looked very distinguished. And all of the Bahamian people knew him. He didn't look Bahamian. He had a very distinct look. He was about an inch shorter than I, standing at about six-feet two- inches. As we parked the car outside the jazz club and got out, we walked side-by-side toward the club, when a man who was passing by stopped and said, "Guy, your son looks just like you."

"Papa, who was that?" I asked.

"I don't know Robaire. But you see that you are definitely your father's son?" I felt great that people thought we looked alike.

We went inside of this funky little jazz club called 'The Chateau' and I sat down while Guy took out his tenor sax and began warming up with his trio. He ran through some scales and shocked me with his proficiency. Marianne hadn't told me that he was a great saxophone player because she probably hadn't even known. But I had a collection of over three hundred jazz compact discs and most of them were by the likes of John Coltrane, Charlie Parker, Cannonball Adderly, Pharoh Sanders, Sonny Rollins, Dexter Gordon, and on and on. So I knew a good tenor sax player when I heard one. He opened the set with a wonderful classic by Charlie Parker, 'Round Midnight,' and it left me with goose bumps on my skin. He freaked me out. He was not American in the slightest, yet he took an American jazz standard and played the hell out of it. He added some blues riffs, and some nice signature lines of his own as well. He received a standing ovation, and I simply shook my head back and forth, wondering what in the world I had been missing out on for over thirty years.

After the show, several spectators wanted his autograph. He obliged them on his way over to the table where his close friend, Antoine Ferrier and I sat. The showman was again replaced by the quiet, almost shy father. Antoine looked at Guy and said something to him in French until Guy admonished him for his rudeness in front of me. "You know Robaire doesn't speak French, Antoine," he said. My father certainly was careful of manners at all times. I appreciated his class.

"What Antoine was saying Robaire, is that you look exactly like your brother Dominique."

Antoine saw my mouth hanging open and added, "You could be twins." I was beyond surprise now. I was just holding on for dear life.

In rapid fire succession my questions came at Guy, "How old is he? Where does he live? What does he do?" Guy's answer was vague as only he could be. I would come to understand this quality in him because it was something I did too. I read him like a book, from the beginning. He was like an onion. You had to peel off layer after layer to get to the truth. But all along the way, the truth was mixed in just enough for him to keep you on your toes. He would have frustrated me too, if we weren't cut from the same mold. He said casually, "I think he is in Paris with his sister Danielle and their mother. He's younger than you, Robaire, by three years, and your sister Danielle is five years younger." I didn't press him because I knew he was gauging me to see how I reacted. He would deal me the whole portion when he was ready, and I would prove my patience to him.

Guy was guarded in everything he said. But I soon began to understand where this was coming from. There were many Haitians who had repatriated to the Bahamas during the dictatorial regime of the Duvaliers in Haiti. Because of his artistic prowess, Guy was often asked to perform for the president, and even to teach his son, 'Baby Doc,' the piano. Some Haitians interpreted his association negatively. Therefore, many times during the week, people would stop him on the street to talk politics with him. "Maestro duRosier," they would holler, "are you a Duvalierist?" What a polarized, political country Haiti is, I realized. This suggestion was tantamount to a slap in the face, considering the common knowledge of the Duvaliers' destruction of Haiti over the course of twenty-eight years of horrifying dictatorial tactics. My father's answer was absolutely brilliant.

"I am a musician. A conductor and arranger of music. The question you should ask is, was Duvalier a duRosierist?"

His accuser was rendered speechless and simply grinned at Guy and walked away. I was in the company of one intelligent man. The way he flipped the coin on that guy was something else. You could not corner this man with language.

I had read nearly every book written on the history of Haiti since first speaking on the phone with Guy so I had a grasp of the volatility that the country suffered politically. Nonetheless, I was hungry for more. The place fascinated me with its mysterious culture that included zombies and voodoo. I asked, "Papa, you let me know when we can go to Haiti together and I am ready."

"I'll let you know Robaire," he said. "You have to meet your grandmother, Mama Francine. She is ninety-three years old. And she is sharp, man." Then my curiosity got the best of me.

"Is voodoo for real?" I asked.

"Robaire, voodoo is the sound of one hand clapping and believe me, you do not want to hear that sound." His answer was mystifying and zen-like but straightforward too. *The sound of one hand clapping.* ' I chewed that one over for a couple of minutes finally admitting that all he had done was pique my curiosity even higher. The famed British author, Graham Greene, wrote what is considered to be the definitive work of literature on Haiti, titled *The Comedians.* In it, he describes actually seeing a zombie and attending voodoo ceremonies. He captures perfectly the dichotomy that is Haiti. Where one can find the finest art in the Western hemisphere, and in the same day see people living in adobe shacks. Or go from the highest French- influenced culture to seeing someone necklaced in the streets of Port au Prince. Necklacing was a terror practice wherein a small tire was fitted around the person's neck and it was filled with gasoline. Once snugly around their neck, the tire was lit on fire and the victim's skull would burn to a crisp. This tactic was used primarily during so-called elections. If you found yourself supporting the unpopular party, you were a candidate to be necklaced by the majority. Politics is serious, serious business in Haiti. There is no freedom of speech, no opposition party.

I could see the agitation on Guy's face over being questioned by that Haitian on the street. I knew not to press him any more about politics, but before I could change the subject, he summarized, "Robaire, most Haitians here in the Bahamas are economic refugees. I have forgotten more about politics than they will ever learn. They are unwashed and unlettered." He delivered this scathing indictment of the illiterate Haitian class that comprised nearly seventy-five percent of the entire country, with a furrowed brow.

"It's disgraceful," he added angrily, "That in a country where education is free, and books are free, these unwashed proliferate and destroy the beauty of Port au Prince." Just like that he was done. My first Haitian political science course was complete. But it was Poly Sci 101: we would graduate quickly to the master's program.

While driving home that night from the gig, Guy searched frantically in the front seat for his cigarettes. When he could not find them he looked over at me and asked, "Robaire, did you sabotage my cigarettes?" I cracked up. His English was sprinkled with French expressions that were so funny.

"Sabotage," I smiled. "No papa, maybe they are in the freezer next to your socks." He laughed riotously exposing a spot in his mouth where his molar used to be. He explained to me that he lost it biting into sugar cane. At least that was a sweet way to lose a tooth. My laughter subsided moments later, however, when I saw something that worried me. While driving, Guy was having small spasms that were causing his right leg to jerk involuntarily. I didn't say anything but I looked at him intently, waiting for him to explain. But he was oblivious to the spasms. I feared he was having what appeared to be symptoms of an epileptic seizure. I let it go in the hope that he would take care of it. I didn't know him well enough after two nights to ask him if he were epileptic.

The next morning, Guy had his ritual cup of coffee. But I called it a cup of sugar with a bit of coffee. I'd never seen someone put so much sugar in coffee. Antoine, Guy's close friend, came by the house to pick us up and take us to his house. The car radio was set on a Haitian channel and I could detect the French and Creole language.

Antoine boisterously directed us, "Attends, attends!!!" On the radio I heard them mention Guy duRosier's name, then some French I could not discern. Next, a song began and Antoine smiled at me and said, "Listen to your father sing on the radio, Robaire." Sure enough I heard my father's voice singing a beautiful song. It was surrealistic, sitting in a car with my father while his music played on the radio.

We arrived at Antoine's house and his wife made me my first Haitian meal. It was delicious. Then Antoine motioned me into the living room where he had an impressive record collection. He pulled out about ten to twelve records and handed them to me. They were all Guy's.

Antoine said proudly, "Your father is too quiet to talk about his music, so I will have to tell you. He is the greatest musician Haiti has ever known. He has been rich many times, only to spend it all on airplanes and cars," he laughed. "He has diplomatic status as Minister of Cultural Affairs when he travels abroad." I looked over at Guy and he was yawning, completely disinterested in Antoine's ringing endorsement. He almost looked embarrassed.

"Antoine, play some samba for Robaire and me," Guy demanded. "He's got plenty of time to hear my music."

The samba rhythm was infectious. It was a blast to simply sit there with my father, listening to music. Neither of us spoke, we were just absorbed in the music.

After the track concluded, Guy said to me, "If you go to Brazil, you may forget that the rest of the world even exists. When I was there for Carnival people actually danced themselves to death. That is passion. My brother August went there eight years ago, and we haven't heard from him since."

These artistic endeavors, sprinkled with impossibly poignant and lyrical conversations with Guy, filled my days and nights in Nassau. We talked about everything from politics to religion and philosophy. During the middle of our discussions, he would stop, put his huge hand over his head and say, "My son, what an intellectual. God is good. *Bon dieu, bon dieu.*"

Finally, the time had come for me to leave Nassau. I hated to leave Guy because I found myself in him. He was my compass. But I knew it was just the beginning of some great, great things to come.

"You have saved my life, Robaire. You are my hero," Guy whispered into my ear, then kissed me on my forehead.

I hugged him closely and said, "I love you immensely Papa."

"I shiver when you call me papa. It has recomposed me." He was reaching into his briefcase looking for something to give me, and he added, "Please tell the Bannisters that I will never forget them in my prayers, and also please take good care of your mother. See to it with discretion that she knows papa Guy still loves her."

"I sure will papa." He had located what he was looking for and reached across to hand me something.

"Robaire I give you this without vanity, it is simply something for you to read so that you know a little more about your father." It was a photocopy of a New York Times critique of one of Guy's concerts. I hugged him goodbye for the last time and promised to call as soon as I returned home. I was back in the air again, on the little twelve-seater headed for Miami. Oddly, I hadn't been in the sun much at all. We didn't go to the beach once. We were too busy getting to know each other and talking all day long.

I decided to look closer at the photocopy that Guy handed me while boarding the flight. What I found in the fine print was that it wasn't just any concert critique. It was a Carnegie Hall concert:

New York Times , Wednesday, May 4ᵗʰ, 1969

SINGER—ORGANIST

VARIES PROGRAM

Guy duRosier touches Haiti, Spain, Paris, and Broadway.

BY JOHN B. WILSON

Guy duRosier, a singer and organist from Haiti, offered a varied program last night at Carnegie Hall. Although Mr. duRosier is billed as "The Living Breath of Haiti," a description applied to him by Edith Piaf when she heard him in Paris, his repertoire spread far beyond his native country.

There were a few nostalgic and spirited references to Haiti in his songs, but he ranged over a wide musical area that included Paris, Broadway, and even Bob Dylan. Seated behind a small electric organ, which was draped with a red and black flag, Mr. duRosier was accompanied by a drummer, Jacques-B Cote, whose style was pure Vaudeville pit band. DuRosier was alternately a dramatic Parisian chansonnier, a robust, full throated black singer, and an organist with a swelling, movie-palace technique.

For the most part, he sang and spoke in French-and his enthusiastic audience revealed themselves as French-speaking by the vociferousness of their response to his comments. But he drifted into English occasionally for a medley from "West Side Story," – delivered with fine theatrical zest as he seemingly sang every role while playing a full orchestral accompaniment on the organ for "Try to Remember," and even for "Lady of Spain," which started out with bravura organ flourishes. Mr. duRosier had the skill to approach all his material, varied as it was in style and origin, with assurance.

But he was at his best in the subtler things, in songs such as "Les prenoms de Paris" and "Ne dis rien," when he could combine his vocal finesse and his smooth organ background most effectively.

Mr. duRosier was the second black performer to give a solo concert at the famed venue, Carnegie Hall, preceded only by Harry Belafonte.

What in the world was I supposed to think? In July of 1969 I was a six-year-old boy standing in Ivo Bannister's garage asking him if he knew anything about my mother and father. On the other side of the United States, in the center of the stage of the most famous performance venue in the world, sat my father behind a keyboard draped patriotically with the Haitian flag, in front of a packed Carnegie Hall. Pride doesn't begin to capture the emotion that filled me that day. I was alive, vibrant, even intimidated somewhat by my pedigree that had been laid bare before me. I was going to have a lot to talk about with Marianne when I returned to Seattle. I was going to ask her how in the world she ended up with my father. She was like a pioneer. Marianne danced to her own beat. She had to be a free spirit to bring me into this world. And boy did she choose an interesting fellow to do it with. In seven days it was clear that Guy was the most intelligent, accomplished man I had ever known. Not just because he was my father. He showed me glimpses of masterful knowledge of philosophy, history, religion, music, politics and more. Not to mention language. He was fluent in all of the Latin languages and conversational even in German. However, Marianne was as sweet and honest as Guy was intellectual, so I understood the combination and how they must have come to love each other. The fact that they were apart seemed counterintuitive. I knew that they both were very happy with me and that our relationships would continue to evolve. But I also knew that personally neither of them was happy. We were a trio of love with the one thing in common being me. Maybe I was, in my own unassuming way, exactly what Guy had called me: an alchemist, the philosophical stone. It wasn't every day that someone called me those terms so I went straight to the dictionary for my edification. *The American Heritage Dictionary* defined alchemy as such:'A medieval chemical philosophy having as its asserted aims the transmutation of base metals into gold, the discovery of the panacea, and the preparation of the elixir of longevity'. I understood his metaphysical assertion to mean that I was responsible for taking two separate entities and changing them, along with myself, into one unit that was better than its individual parts. I thought I was deep. All of my life I had known certain things about life instinctually. I had never once felt like I couldn't hold my own spiritually with any individual I had ever met. Further, I felt more enlightened even as a child than most anybody I had ever known, young or old. Buy my father was deep, deeper, and deepest. He really was more spirit than matter. "*The Haitian Sensation,*" I laughed quietly.

On the ground in Miami I had enough time to phone Marianne. I knew she would be at work so I called her there.

"I know you're busy Mom, but I just wanted to check in with you. That is the most interesting man I have ever met, mom, and we have got one heck of a lot to talk about tonight."

She said, "I told you, so Robert. Didn't I say that your father was something else?"

I got home that evening and again felt that chill hit my bones. I made a vow to myself right then and there that I would not die in Seattle. It sounds morbid, but I knew that if I were an old man, that cold, wet weather would fill my lungs with pneumonia and kill me.

Marianne was practically waiting by the front door for me. She opened it before I could put my hand on the doorknob.

"Hi Mom, I sure do love you. And I've got tons of pictures for you to see."

"Oh goody, let's get them developed right now." She was curious to see what Guy looked like after thirty-one years.

"That man is too much," I said as I shook my head back and forth. "He's just like me, Mom."

She corrected me, "You mean you're just like him."

"Yeah," I smiled, "I guess he was here first, huh? He's so cool! He's really unique-looking and graceful. And so elegant, mom."

"Your momma done good, didn't she?" Marianne beamed.

"Yeah, you know how to pick 'em Redhead."

"Go get the pictures developed Robert," she interrupted.

"Okay, Mom, I'll take them to the one-hour developer." I wasn't finished talking about Guy though, "Mom, he is friends with Sidney Poitier. And he is good friends with the Bahamian Ambassador to Great Britain. But he's like the wacky professor. One minute he's receiving a standing ovation from the audience, the next he's asking me where his glasses are and they're right on his face," I laughed. Marianne roared along with me on the front porch.

"I'll be back in an hour, Mama," I said.

"Hurry right back, Robert."

She came in my room looking like a five-year-old on Christmas morning. "Get those pictures open," she demanded.

"Patience Redhead, patience." I took my sweet time just to annoy her. Then I spread out two full rolls of film on the bed. Forty-eight exposures of the love of her youth. I wondered if thirty years were longer for a son who never saw his parents, or for a woman who hadn't seen her lover. Time is not always equal.

"This one is especially for you, Mom," I said. It was a picture of Guy holding his sax in one hand and blowing her a kiss with the other. She put her hand over her mouth and her face turned red. She loved the pictures, and she looked at them over and over again.

I had to look for a place of my own to live because I wanted to be able to have Guy visit me in Seattle. I tried to break the news gently to Marianne as she continued to scan the photos.

"Mom, I love living here with you, but I've got to get a place so that Papa can come visit. We talked about him coming out here soon. And I certainly can't bring him around with Ken here."

She got a very concerned look on her face and pleaded with me, "You can't leave me here. I want to move out with you. You've got to get me out of jail, Robert." I did a quick double take. I looked at Marianne inquisitively.

"You're not kidding me, are you, Mom?"

"No," she said. "You've seen how Ken and I are. We're just friends. It's hardly what I call a marriage." I wasn't shocked. I knew she wasn't happy, but I didn't anticipate that she would actually move out. That did shock me.

"Mom, I am staying so far out of that. I don't want to touch that one." I did welcome her to look at apartments with me though. "I'll get a two bedroom place, and you will be the only roommate that I'll have. It'll be open for you if you in fact decide you want to leave. We would make terrific roommates, Mom!"

She urged, "I'm ready to go today, Robert. Let's go look for a place."

Guy and I had decided that we would phone each other on Sundays. I looked forward to those days for the bonding that they provided.

The first Sunday back, I had to ask him about the Carnegie Hall show. "Papa, the article said that you were the second black solo performer to have ever played there. That's amazing!"

He said, "Yes Robaire, I was fortunate to be discovered in Nassau by the Lady Eunice Oakes, who was the widow of the late Andrew Carnegie. She saw me perform and invited me that same day to play Carnegie."

Marianne was making it a point to be home on Sundays. At first, she and Guy would exchange pleasantries sandwiched around my conversation. Then, things began to slowly change. They were spending more and more time on the phone, and I was exchanging quick visits with Guy. I was amazed. If it would have been discreet to do so, they wouldn't have had to channel their conversations through me, but it was safer this way.

9

PAIN

I WONDERED, as I drove back to my old neighborhood to visit Ivo and Ione Bannister, if all grown kids got a foreboding, nauseating feeling when returning to the place of their youth. It was a place that I endured more than thrived in. It was not, however, without its great memories too. I had friends lined up and down the street. There was George, my very first friend, and Allen, and Carla, my first little girlfriend in kindergarten. It was a normal American middle-class neighborhood complete with some woods nearby where I almost coughed up a lung with George as we experimented with our first and last cigarette. And there was the 7-11, our major candy and slurpy supplier. We'd drink our slurpies so fast in the summertime that our brains would freeze up in pain. Then there was the vacant lot where I enjoyed some of the most intense wiffle-ball games a kid could have. We even had a homemade scoreboard and we'd play until dark all summer long. I saw the various lawns that I mowed for spending money, but they didn't look the same. They were haggard and unkempt. I had those lawns looking like putting greens when I was twelve or thirteen.

As I made that familiar left-hand turn at the bottom of the steep hill, I looked to my right at the brick house on the corner. There it was, the Bannisters'. The hill was long and very steep. It was symbolic of my entire life. It was on that hill that I had my first broken bone. A bunch of the neighborhood kids were trying to make it all the way to the bottom on skateboards. I had just pitched a game for my sixth-grade team at Our Lady of Lourdes against St. Edwards. I was still in my uniform when I was the first one to make it all the way down without falling. But at the bottom of the hill I fell face-first and landed on my wrist, shattering it. It killed me. There was searing pain when I tried to move my fingertips, and I knew this was no ordinary pain. I hid in the basement out of the fear that Ivo Bannister would find out. But when my friend George was unable to make me laugh or even smile, he knew something was wrong too. He had never seen me cry so hard, and by the look on his face, it scared him. He told me he was going to get my dad, and I pleaded for him not to. Minutes later I could hear the heavy, plodding footsteps of those steel-toed boots. He was coming. He saw me curled up in a ball and said, "What the hell's going on here, Bobby Jo?"

After I told him, he wanted to know if I could move my wrist. I tried and it hurt.

He said, "Looks like a sprain. You'll be all right in a day or two." Then he walked off. That evening I lay squirming in pain in my bed. I was trying as hard as I could to lie perfectly still so that the pain wouldn't kill me. It hurt even when I inhaled and exhaled. Two days later, I was taken to the doctor, where I had my arm cast.

Years later during high school, I used that hill for conditioning. What I didn't realize back then was that I was conditioning my mind as well as my body. I ran wind sprints up the hill, usually about twenty-five sets or to exhaustion. It strengthened my legs for baseball but it also was my silent, difficult companion. When I felt like I couldn't do another set, it wasn't baseball or physical prowess that steeled my determination to do another. No, it was my life. I had to keep going. I couldn't let that hill, as ominous as it looked from the bottom, get to me mentally. The more the lactic acid burned through my legs, the more I liked it. The pain took my mind off of the more threatening pain associated with my life. The neighbors always commented from their car windows while driving up or down and passing me, "Must be baseball season huh, Bobby?" I'd wave and grin at them. They probably thought Floyd's younger brother really wanted to make it to the big leagues too. They were wrong. I ran that hill for my sanity. I needed something to so completely physically exhaust me, that the pain would take my mind completely off of the pain of my life.

Still, it wasn't the neighbors, the house, or streets that made me uneasy to return. It was the precarious perch that I occupied inside of that house on the corner. It was the unstable stability that turned my stomach.

There was a diameter out of which the Bannister children were not allowed. It was usually the farthest distance from which we could hear Ione's whistle. If you were not seated at the dinner table within five minutes of that whistle, you had to deal with Ivo. He had a two-sided leather strap with a clip at the top that hung ominously just inside the back yard door. He'd make us go and get it for him and then he'd yell down at us with an angry face, "How old are you?" And our age was the number of times we'd be whipped with that strap. Now if you were eight and you said you were two, he didn't laugh a bit. You'd get ten. The scariest thing about the whippings was not the actual strap. It was the way he bowed the two pieces of leather out wide and then violently snapped them together, making a terrifying popping sound. Even if I had to choke on my tongue, I tried my hardest never to cry. At those moments I hated his guts and I didn't want to let him see me cry. I knew I would never stand over my kids and brow beat them or worse, simply beat them. Even as a kid I knew he lacked the emotional control that an adult should possess. There was something worse than anger behind his eyes: it was meanness.

When I heard that whistle, I sprinted home from George's house as fast as I could. I was out of the bathroom with cleansed hands and at the table first or second, usually. There were anywhere from five to seven of us kids at any given time, and sometimes even more, depending on how many foster kids were currently there. Hands were folded, and in Catholic tradition we all recited, "Bless us oh Lord, and these thy gifts, which we are about to receive, from thy bounty, through Christ our Lord, Amen." Then dinner was on. Ivo called it supper. And he called Ione, "Mom." She called him, "Dad." That always bugged me for some reason. I wondered why they didn't call each other by their names. I buried my head in my mashed potatoes and gravy on a nightly basis. I sat still, but I always bristled when they cursed. I knew, even as a kid, that they shouldn't use certain words. But the worst was when they used racial slang to describe our new neighbors who had moved next door. I hated their guts every time they called our neighbors "niggers, chocolate drops, Hershey kisses, coons, or tar babies," and on and on. And it was the tricky way they said it and the guilty pleasure they derived from almost whispering, but not quietly enough to conceal their ignorance from a table full of seven children. The "Oh, they're from South Dakota, or they're from a different generation," defense just never washed with me. I knew that they knew it was wrong by the way they said things in hushed tones.

After dinner, Floyd and I would bolt outside and turn on the flood-lights to play baseball or basketball. The dishes were always left to the girls. It was always weird when Ivo would hang around in the kitchen and take a towel, roll it up and snap it at one of his daughter's back-sides. He'd chuckle, and I'd pretend not to see it keeping my disdain to myself. There was nothing like disdain on the face of a child to infuri-ate a grownup. I took notes on a regular basis in that house. Mental notes on how not to act!

If putting food on the table, clothes on backs, and a roof overhead is the great equalizer, then so be it. I think a person is either kind, or they're not. And the tone in the Bannister home was set from the top down. The beauty of a large family, though, is that it is easy to become semi-invisible. It's easy to observe from a distance.

Ione was kind overall but voiceless. That was a generational issue. Women seldom worked, or even drove for that matter. So even though she was vastly and obviously Ivo's intellectual superior, she was emo-tionally under his thumb.

They were from Pierre, South Dakota and were neighbors. Their very names made them sound like a match set. Ivo and Ione. Ivo dropped out of school after the eighth grade to help work for his fam-ily and then he joined the service as soon as he was of age. After he got out of the army, he worked for the railroad putting down ties.

Ione graduated high school and came from an educated family. Her mother, Pearl, had graduated from a teacher's college and taught school for over twenty-five years. Ione became pregnant with Louise, the el-dest Bannister child, in Pierre, South Dakota, while Ivo was working the railroad. Ivo's sister, Beatrice, had moved to Seattle and found em-ployment with the Boeing Company. She wrote to Ivo informing him of the opportunity for employment as a machinist. Soon Ivo, Ione and family were moving to Seattle, Washington. This house was their first and only home they'd ever owned. They had five more children of their own before their association with the Catholic Children's Service's or-phanage as an interim foster care home provider.

They looked like a Norman Rockwell painting. He, with his Osh Kosh coveralls and hat with the bill flipped up. And she, standing be-side her man, solemn-faced and overweight, with an apron around her waist. They said things like, "winder," instead of "window," and "perti-neer," instead of "almost." They couldn't have gotten me to speak that way if they had put a gun to my head.

I parked my little red Honda CRX in the familiar but old driveway. I collected the albums with Guy's image on them and gathered them up to proceed inside the house. Even though the reception I got the last time I spoke to Ivo and Ione was chilly concerning the reunion with Marianne, I never would want to keep from them the fact that I had found my father too. I wanted to be forthcoming and to attempt to share this as much as I could with them. If I owed them anything at all, it was that. Full disclosure. They did deserve that. I looked at it as an opportunity to get closer to them, because despite all of our obvious differences, they did raise me. I was, in fact, alive and well. I was a well-educated, productive adult. I was giving them another opportunity to share in my private life and to include them in something very, very important to me.

Ione opened the door and hollered, "Bobby's here." Ivo strolled over and said, "Put 'er there, young man," with hand extended. I shook his hand firmly and walked inside the house that now seemed tiny. There were two other people in the room, friends of theirs from the neighbor-hood. There wasn't much we could talk about but we tried until finally some small talk led to the reason I was there.

"I brought some things for you to see. I just returned from the Bahamas and spent a week with my biological father, Guy duRosier, as you already know."

They both nodded their heads.

"He specifically asked me to tell you that he will always remember you in his prayers."

Ivo said, "Did you say on the phone you were going to bring some pictures of him?"

"Yes," I answered, "I've got one of his record albums right here." I pulled out the record and sat it down in the middle of the dining room table where the six of us sat. They all passed it around and looked at it when it finally ended up in Ione's hands last. She studied it momen-tarily, looked up at me and said, "I see a resemblance, but you don't have the nigger wool hair like he does." She held it up for the neighbors to see, and added, "Bobby doesn't have the nigger look like he does."

My eyes began to burn and sting the way they do when you go a long time without blinking. My heart started beating fast and my throat constricted. I felt like a kid, back at the dinner table listening to garbage come out of their mouths but being the good, compliant child, never wanting to rock the boat. But I was no longer the compliant child. I was however, a peaceful man, who was always careful and measured in my response to stimulus. Oh the irony of it all! My father, the most intellectual, accomplished man I knew, was reduced to the status of a "nigger," by the people who raised me. And to add insult, this was done in mixed company. In front of two other people I didn't even know. His message was gracious. *Tell them they are in my prayers always.* Their reply was pure hatred. And they cut me to the bone the way nobody else could have. I had to get out of there before I turned that table upside down and gave them the condensed, unrated version of thirty-one years' worth of what I thought of them. I stood up, pulled my chair back and leaned across the table to take the record out of Ione's hand.

"Excuse me," I said as I turned my back to them, breezed through the back porch screen door like I had done a thousand times over in my youth, and pulled out of that driveway as quickly as I could. I hated that place and everything about it. I hated the rockery that ran alongside the house as I drove down the hill. I hated the tree on the corner as I sped off at the stop sign. I hated the neighbor's house. I hated the road I was driving on. I simply just hated until I was forced to pull off of the side of the road a few miles away because I was crying so hard I couldn't see the road. Everything was a blur. My head felt heavy and I leaned forward until my forehead lay against the top of the steering wheel. I sobbed until my rib cage felt broken. I pulled into a convenience store and dialed Marianne. Fortunately, she answered. She couldn't understand me through my sobbing. She had never heard me like this before.

"Robert, what's the matter? You've got to tell me what's the matter?" she implored. I was a mess. I was crying the way little kids do when they can't catch their breath.

"Mom, they did it. They called him a nigger right to my face. They called him a nigger. How could they do that to me, and in front of their friends too? Ione said it, Mom. God damn them to hell."

Marianne was worried about me. All she could say, and she repeated it over and over was, "Shame on them. Shame, shame, shame." She asked me if I'd like her to come pick me up, and I thanked her but assured her I would be all right in a few minutes.

"I'm going to wait to get on the road for a few minutes, then I'll see you in a little while Mom."

Marianne said to me in a way that could not be mistaken, "I love you, Robert." She was performing emergency surgery on my broken, shattered heart.

I soon regained my composure. I knew that I had to accept the seasons of my heart, just as I would recognize the seasons of the year. I was going to somehow accept, with serenity, this winter of my grief.

10

PLEASURE

I stood in front of the judge at the Monroe County Courthouse and listened attentively to his inquiries as to the reason for my request for change-of- name. Typically, this was done when females took their husbands last name, but mine was the atypical case.

"Are you attempting to evade any liens, judgments, or debts of any kind against you?" asked the judge.

"No sir. May I explain the circumstances that have led me to this decision?"

"Go ahead."

"I recently have met both my biological mother and father, sir. After spending time with my father, it is my understanding that I must take my rightful last name. We grew very, very, close and it is his full expectation that I carry his last name."

I was prepared to elaborate further when he interrupted my thoughts and said, "Approved. Please pay the cashier fifty five dollars on your way out." He signed some paperwork and passed it to the clerk.

I waited in the lobby for the cashier. The documents were given to me. They stated, "On this date, August 8, 1993, the Monroe County Court does hereby authorize the change of name from Robert J. Bannister, to Robert J. duRosier."

I had to change my passport, my driver's license, my employee identification at Alaska Airlines, my insurance and benefits, even my Blockbuster card. It was like I was marrying Guy. That cracked me up.

I told Marianne, "I love him and all, but there is a limit. I feel like I'm Papa's woman." We laughed and laughed.

"Robert duRosier. Oh how that name suits you. It sounds so much better."

People at work and old friends butchered my name until I sounded it out phonetically for them. I could hardly blame them though, because not many people in Seattle spoke French. "No," I'd constantly correct them. "It is not Durocher." They had me confused with the old pro ball player Leo Durocher. "It is du, like the morning 'dew', rose, just like it sounds, 'ee', like the letter 'e', 'ay', like the letter 'a'. Now, say it like there is a chance you may some day go to Paris. Put a French accent behind it and remember the 'r', on the end is silent. Say it like inspector Clouseau from the 'Pink Panther' would."

If Guy had heard some of the botched pronunciations, he would have used some funny word like, 'sabotage.' I could just hear it, "Robaire, why do they sabotage such a beautiful name?" His lips would have been pursed and his eyebrows furrowed over two squinting eyes. He was a snob sometimes, the way only the French could be.

It wasn't long before all of my documentation was intact. Some things took longer than others to change over, but I was a new man. I had the same Social Security Number so often I would have to explain the name change, and I grew accustomed to actually carrying the court order in my wallet for proof. I took my time breaking the news to my brother and sisters from the Bannisters. I hadn't spoken to Ivo and Ione and didn't intend to anytime soon.

I loved hearing my name called out loud. "Table for two for duRosier," for example, sounded like music to my ears. Or I'd hear my name on a prerecorded list of flight attendants on call for trips. It was like regaining a piece of my birthright. Nobody could rewind and do their life over, but I had something that was all mine. It defined me and addressed who I really was. I was just as exotic as my last name sounded. Bannister was a German last name. I didn't have a drop of German blood in me. "Bannister," like Guy said, "was rented."

It was hard to believe that it was coming up on our second holiday season together. Thanksgiving was just around the corner and it brought back fond memories of my first Christmas with Marianne. I got Guy on my passes at Alaska Airlines so he had free flight privileges too. And I talked him into coming to stay with me for Christmas.

The apartment that I found was a two-bedroom place just like I had told Marianne. I was afraid to get in her business any further. I was going to leave her alone to decide what she wanted to do. I was flying so much that the only day I had available to move was on Thanksgiving Day. I was actually working that morning and had a twenty-four-hour layover in Portland. So instead of sitting in the hotel all day long, I caught a flight back to Seattle and moved my things out of Ken and Marianne's house. It took me about four trips back and forth by myself. The snow from the previous evening was packed and icy around the steps to my new apartment, making my move that much more difficult. I carried a box spring mattress over my shoulder up two flights of stairs while most people were eating turkey or watching football. They must have thought I was nuts. But I was on a mission because it was the only day I had available to move, and Guy was coming in a few days. By nightfall I had finished and hurried back to the airport to catch a flight back to Portland so that I could continue with my trip the following morning.

When I returned to my new place the next day, I was thrilled to see Marianne's things in the apartment as well. I shook my head back and forth, "*She really did it! Man, what a woman. This little redhead does what, and only what, she wants to do.*" What I realized when I saw her bedroom furniture and boxes in the hallway, was that she was in fact going to be able to spend time with Guy now. She wouldn't have been able to before.

I did the math in my head. He was coming to stay with me, she lived with me; therefore, we were going to be together, the three of us, like a real family. I scolded myself for allowing even the thought of such a thing to enter my mind in Nassau, but just a few short months later, it was going to become a reality. Unbelievable!

The front door opened, and there stood Marianne whom I adored more than ever. "Momma, you did it. We're actually going to be roommates. You are a bold woman."

She beamed. She had a determined look on her face and answered, "There's no way I was going to stay out there, Robert. He can find a new maid and cook because that's all I was, essentially."

I was excited but I was also feeling a bit guilty. "Mom, I hope I didn't cause you any trouble." She reassured me that it was her decision entirely, and that she thought about doing it long, long ago.

"You know who's going to be here next week, don't you?" I played.

Marianne was unable to contain a huge smile that spread out across her beautiful face. The eyes were twinkling again. She gave me a mischievous look and admitted, "We talked on the phone yesterday while you were flying."

"Ah huh," I huffed. "You have graduated. You don't have to go through me anymore. That's great." I asked her, "What exactly is going on between you two?" She grinned at me and that said it all. "Okay Momma, I get it. This is unreal." Marianne mentioned that we had better get some furniture. We had nothing in the front room at all. She took care of that, and by the time I got home from flying my weekend trip, we had a beautifully furnished place to live.

The three-day trip I was on seemed like a thirty- day trip. I knew that when I returned to Seattle on Monday evening, Guy would be there with Marianne waiting for me. I just didn't know what to expect. The anticipation was killing me. I figured Marianne must have been having the same feelings. The last leg home from San Francisco was delayed by about an hour. I saw the delay on the board in the terminal and I was very agitated. But finally we taxied into Sea-Tac Airport, and I set a new record for getting out of there. I was off of the shuttle bus and into my car in no time at all.

The closer I got to home the more nervous I became. In all of my years of prayers and tears, I never even supposed that I could have my mother and father together. That was too unreasonable a request, even of God. I had stuck to the basics and simply asked for my mother. Getting my father back was a bonus, and an unexpected miracle at that. Now, to have them together in the same room with me was more than I could have ever dreamed. Something like 'divine intervention' came to mind as I drove along I-405, hurrying toward Kirkland.

I felt like an actor rehearsing his lines before the curtain came up. I was having the most incredible internal dialogue with myself. I could say this, or that, or hug them, or any number of different things. I carried on imaginary conversations until I knew that what I would do was simply whatever the moment felt like. I was never the nervous type and it certainly wasn't time to start being nervous now.

I parked the car, reached into the hatchback, collected my suitcase, and proceeded up the stairs to the front door. I stepped inside of the door slowly, pulling my suitcase closely behind. I looked up before I was all the way through the door, and I saw them. Guy and Marianne were arm in arm on the sofa, lying comfortably together like sweethearts. She was curled up around him, cuddling closely.

They both were staring right at me, and I glanced first at my mother, then my father. Happiness radiated from within both of them. They were so relaxed. The contrast in their skin color was terrific. What a gorgeous couple they were. I had sensory overload. I still hadn't moved inside the door or said anything, I was just looking, when finally, Guy said, "Marianne, did we do that?" He was pointing at me and referring to their pride at having produced me. "Look at the face, so candid, so handsome," he beamed. She didn't say a word but simply tried to tuck her face even deeper into Guy's shoulder. I was looking at two people obviously in love, and I couldn't believe it.

"Hi Papa, hi Redhead," I said as I finally came into the house. "You two should see what I see right now. I'm looking at the most beautiful vision I've ever seen in my entire life."

I moved around to the kitchen to get something to drink, and Guy and Marianne stood up to walk over. They stood across from me and Guy said, "If God made anything more beautiful than your mother, then surely he has kept it all to himself."

Marianne looked drunk with passion. And Guy did not call her Marianne. Instead he called her 'Anne Marie.' The French pronunciation of that name sounded exquisite, and it did not escape the affection of Marianne.

She said she was tired and that she was going to bed. Guy stayed behind to talk with me for a few moments. "I'll be right there, darling," he said to Marianne.

"Robaire," Guy said earnestly to me, "thank you, my son, for delivering your mother back to my arms where she belongs. And thank you for your forgiveness. You have endured to live a life that was unintended for you. And you have forgiven without even trying. You've done it instinctively, naturally. Your clemency has not gone unnoticed by your father. I believe that clemency is the highest of virtues and you, my son, are a virtuous man. Papa is proud." With that, he took my head in his massive hands and pulled me toward him to deliver a kiss on my forehead. "Robaire, be assured that I would never hurt your mother, not even with the petal of a rose."

I gasped at the beauty of what he just said.

"Bon nuit, Robaire. A demain, mon enfant."

"Bon nuit, Papa." He had called me his infant.

He looked back over his shoulder at me before entering Marianne's bedroom and said forcefully, "Remember, we are black like the ink of soul." He smiled then and said, "Papa is enchanted."

Whenever Guy spoke, it took me time to digest everything he had just said. Because it was so lyrical, so beautiful that you could simply swim around in his prose. He had the consideration to tell me he would never hurt my mother. I knew that it took a virtuous man to recognize another. I loved that man with every fiber of my being.

I lay awake in bed that evening, replaying the evening over and over in my head. The look on Marianne's face was so wonderful. She hardly spoke because she was so overcome with love and passion for Guy. And Guy was tender with her the way that no other man had been since the summer of 1962 in Vancouver, B.C. I had been from Phoenix, to Seattle, to Nassau, Bahamas and back, and I had constructed the life I had dreamed of. I built it from scratch and now I sat back and reveled in what was the crowning achievement of my life thus far. Just as I was oblivious to the clemency that I extended Guy, I was most certainly also an inadvertent matchmaker. Guy saw the shape of what was becoming from the very beginning. But I was too busy acting to know what I was piecing together.

When you are able to smile at night in the solitude of your bed, a huge smile that comes from the heart, you must be in heaven.

The following evening we decided to go out to a restaurant together for dinner. It was the first time that the three of us were out together in public. I was, by this time in my life, very much used to the looks from other people. I could nearly read their minds. Most of my life, the looks said, "They all look like a family, except he looks different. He can't be their kid." It was obvious in the way that the look lasted about three seconds longer than it should have. The scanning always went from the Bannisters, to me, then back to them. I grew to expect it and tried not to let it bother me. This evening, the looks were different. They saw us as a unit. Any lingering looks now were because of the bi-racial nature of our family.

Guy was smartly dressed in a navy blue suit, and Marianne was lovely in her light blue dress. He quickly moved to pull her chair out for her, then sat her down at the table first. He stood until both she and I were seated, then sat down himself. It shouldn't have been that impressive, but it was. He had impeccable manners. I would expect any man to have demonstrated that kind of etiquette, but it just didn't exist that often anymore. It got the attention of several couples dining around us.

"Robaire," Guy worried, "I see no other black people here. Are we safe here?"

I laughed, "Oh yeah Papa, we're safe. Don't worry at all. If somebody wanted to get to you, they would have to go through me first and they don't want any part of that."

Guy's tension eased noticeably.

Marianne was glowing like a tiki lamp on a steamy, summer evening. I had never seen her beaming the way she was. She had the tired, relaxed look of a lover in the afterglow of passion. They looked spectacular together. I was so proud to be together like I had seen families all of my life. I had a beautiful mother and an elegant father. I was a part of a family that I wasn't trying to hide from. I was like a duck on the pond. On the surface everything looked calm, but underneath those little feet were churning a mile a minute.

That evening, Marianne propped herself up in bed on one elbow so that she could watch Guy sleep. It brought back memories of Harrison Hot Springs resort to her. She used to just sit and stare at Guy's face as he slept peacefully. He would wake suddenly and ask, "Why were you watching me, darling?" She'd say honestly, "You have got the most interesting face that I've ever seen."

Guy basked in her compliments like a child winning his first trophy. He loved the compliments in the way that only an artist with a fragile ego could. Artists are the ultimate oxymoron in that they put their heart and soul into their work for all the world to critique. You would think that a person like that would be supremely confident, however, they really are the most fragile of souls. So Guy smiled, pulled Marianne closer to him, and said, "Really?"

Marianne knew that was his way of saying, "Tell me more darling."

Marianne wondered how in the world he could have been back in her bed thirty-two years later, lying there with that same handsome, unique, interesting face that captivated her so.

Guy again woke up and Marianne reminded him of how she used to watch him sleep. "Darling," Guy said, "This time it is my turn to watch you sleep."

She curled up into a ball beside him while he rested his head in his large hand. His thumb was curled underneath his chin and his fingers extended all the way up over the top of his head. It looked like the thinking man's pose. He stared at his darling 'Anne-Marie' lovingly while she drifted off into a deep, peaceful sleep.

Later the next day, Guy was restless. It was nearly four o'clock in the afternoon and we had been relaxing most of the day. I could see him getting more and more anxious with every moment.

"Papa, what's up with you?"

He kept looking out the window minute by minute. "I am looking for your mother, my Anne-Marie to return home to me from work," he said. He could hardly stand being away from her for the eight hours that her job as a dietician required. When her car pulled up into the lot, he jumped from the sofa with glee and did a little voodoo dance all the way over to the front door. He cracked me up. He was like a teenager! He held the door open for Marianne like a valet. He greeted her at the door with a hug and a kiss and said, "My Cherie, your absence has pained me today. But I am recomposed as we speak." She tenderly placed her palm on his cheek and kissed him passionately on the mouth. I watched the whole thing in amazement. That was what I always thought lovers were supposed to act like.

As Marianne moved into the kitchen to put away some groceries, Guy signaled for me to stand up beside him where she could hear the two of us. We had been rehearsing that day a song that he wrote for her. We had the harmonization down pat. And it was beautiful indeed. "Let's lay it on her, Robaire," Guy said to me.

"Okay, Papa."

Guy asked Marianne, "Darling will you please put down the groceries so that we can show you what we've done for you today?" She looked stunned and excited. She turned and looked at us both wide-eyed. Then Guy counted, "*Un, deux, trois, …*" and we broke into song for her:

"*And then God reached with his hand*
And he took the light
He rolled the light in his hand, in his hand, in his hand,
Rolled the light in his hand 'till he made your lovely eyes,
And made your body of fire.
Marianne duRosier,
Marianne duRosier,

Anne-Marie duRosier,
Is the woman God made the best.

It was short but sweet. It had a wonderful Caribbean flavor to it and we sang it Calypso style for her. She started to dance half way through the song and by the time we were finished her cheeks were flushed with color and her eyes were dancing around like shimmering stars.

She was very happy. She joked, "Wow, what a way to come home from work."

Guy smiled, "Cheri, I'm telling you that Haitians don't mess around."

I interrupted, "Mom, you should have seen the voodoo dance papa did across the living room to the front door when he saw your car pull up."

She wanted to see it. Guy looked at her and did the coolest dance I'd ever seen. He rolled his shoulders and moved his hips rhythmically reminiscent of an African ritual dance, which, in fact, is exactly what a voodoo dance was. If we had had a conga player in the room, we may have been able to do some magic. She was mesmerized by it all. I looked across the room at her and shook my head back and forth, chuckling to myself. I wondered aloud, "What in the world have I done?" I found Marianne and now her life was turned upside down. One thing was certain, she was definitely living.

I rented a Yamaha keyboard so that Guy would have something to arrange with. He was in the mood to release his first recording in years.

"Robaire," he said to me, "I am going to put Haiti back on the map with my next release. It will flip them out. And the timing is perfect, with Haiti in the news everyday."

There had been a coup in Haiti that June just as Guy predicted. The first democratically-elected president in Haiti's history, Jean Bertrand Aristide, was exiled to the United States, leaving the General of the Army, Raoul Cedras, in power. This created an extremely volatile situation in Haiti. In essence, it came down to a battle of power between the bourgeoisie versus the illiterate peasant class. The bourgeoisie was opposed to the proletariat in the class struggle. President Aristide played the proletariat like a well-tuned violin. He appealed to them by addressing the nation in Creole, which no other Haitian president had done. By the sheer size of their numbers, they carried him to a surprising victory. The educated Haitian only spoke Creole if addressed in Creole.

Guy said, "I would never engage someone in Creole. I speak French first."

I began to get a better understanding than any of the history books on Haiti could give me. It had been this way since the country won its independence from Napoleon's France in 1803. The price of Haiti's freedom as the first independent black republic outside of Africa was steep. With it came trade embargoes from every nation. France, Spain, Britian, and the United States, former trade partners in everything from tobacco, rum, cotton, and especially sugar cane, stopped any and all trade with Haiti. This turned the 'Pearl of the Caribbean,' the richest colony in the entire Caribbean, into the poorest country in the Western Hemisphere. The mulatto class in Haiti was the ruling power from the beginning because they inherited land from their French progenitors. This banishment by ostracism created a breeding ground for political, class, and economic corruption. Therefore, a coup was never a surprise in Haiti. In the past, there were bloody coups.

Any man who ascended to the presidency of Haiti immediately began looking over his shoulder. It began with Touissant L'Overture, then Jean Jacque Dessalines, Alexandre Petion, and on. The huge difference with the exiled President Aristide, was that he was the first Haitian president to champion the proletariat. The unwashed, unlettered, peasant class. This was upsetting over a century of established policy in Haiti. And the final straw for Aristide came when he addressed the nation one Sunday and called for the 'necklacing' of the upper- class Haitians. He told the peasants to 'flood Port au Prince and claim your land.' This meant that the once beautiful streets of Port au Prince would be flooded with transients. There would be squatters on peoples' homes. People erecting lean-to's on other's property.

Guy said, "When you asked to come in April, I couldn't allow it because if these unwashed saw our faces, and realized we were well-fed, and literate, we would become candidates for necklacing. I could not subject you to that Robaire. But the climate has changed since Rene Preval has taken the presidency. So we can go to Haiti very soon and record our CD for release while Haiti is in the national spotlight."

I was thrilled to hear him say that we could go to Haiti. I wanted desperately to meet my Grandmother Francine before she died. She was ninety-three years old. And I wanted to see that mysterious little island that so much had been written about.

Marianne loved to watch us rehearse back in the spare bedroom. Guy was teaching me two songs, one in Creole and one in French. The first was a song called "Do-do, Ti-ti." This was a classic children's nursery rhyme much like "Rockabye Baby." However, he rearranged it in the most elegant, beautiful way. We would sing it together in harmonization. He wrote the piece for twelve violins, a viola, cello, oboe, harp, French horns, tenor saxophone, castanets, rain stick, and a background choir.

He said, "When the Haitians hear how this song has been reharmonized and orchestrated, vocalized by father and son, they will faint in their seats. Every Haitian has heard this song in their youth, but I promise you they haven't heard it like this."

We sang it for Marianne and she was astounded. She was surprised at my voice.

"Robert, I had no idea you could sing like that."

Guy intervened, "Marianne, he is a duRosier!"

We all laughed while Marianne said, "I should have known."

My first glimpse of my father on the cover of a record album that Ethel St. Claire mailed to me.

Guy performing with his orchestra in Montreal, Canada.

Guy and Marianne back in each other's arms after thirty years.

Father and son reunited. We are both very happy about it too.

Marianne and I, in Phoenix, Az. 1990.

The Bannisters July 11, 1992.

Me at the age of six - every bit as frightened and sad as I looked.

My daughter, Josette. She looks happier than I ever did in my youth.

My daughter, Josette. Her joy and confidence at the same age is a stark contrast to my photo.

11

THE MAGIC ISLAND

IT was hard to believe that I was headed back to the Caribbean for the third time in nine months, and to the third different island. I had been to Jamaica with Marianne, then to the Bahamas, and now I was on final descent into Port au Prince, Haiti, to meet the rest of my family.

Guy had left Seattle ahead of me to get started laying down the tracks for his latest record. He wanted to get most of the instrumentation done so that by the time I arrived all I'd have to do is go in- studio and lay down my vocal tracks. What an exciting trip I was taking. Not only was I going to meet all of the duRosiers, but I was also going to go into a recording studio for the first time and make a record with my father.

Haiti looked larger and a bit different than the other islands I had seen from the air. It was very, very mountainous. In fact, the native inhabitants, the Arawak Indians, gave Haiti its name, "Ayiti," meaning, "Mountain." I could close my eyes and almost visualize the epic, horrifying battles in the hills between the French army, led by the bloodthirsty, dubious, general Rochambeau and the relentless, displaced Africans mostly from the Ivory Coast, specifically, Guinea. Frustrated and tired from the malaria and the guerilla warfare tactics of the indentured African slaves, General Rochambeau resorted to the most heinous of tactics including, burying slaves alive up to their necks and stuffing every orifice with sugar so that the rodents would eat them alive. Haitian general, Jean Jacques Dessalines, learned from his French counterpart and began to terrorize the French troops with equal passion. He would put the heads of deceased French soldiers on sticks and post them all over the French plantations. This contentious battle for independence finally caught up to the French in what was Napoleon's first defeat. The Haitians had won their independence from France nearly a century before the emancipation proclamation in the United States. Needless to say, the Haitians were a proud people. But since the reign of the demagogue, Francois Duvalier, this little country was not a tourist attraction whatsoever. Haiti was not the island one chose when planning a Caribbean vacation.

It was with these thoughts that I prepared myself for landing in Port au Prince. I could see the airport in the distance and I heard the flight attendants making their landing announcements in French. Enough drama had played out at this little airport to write several books about. It was the scene of numerous late night getaways by presidents in exile seeking asylum in other countries. It was also the scene of many murders of those attempting to escape for political asylum.

I stepped off of the airplane and admittedly felt intimidated by this place. If Guy were not here, I would never come by myself. But Guy was planning on picking me up, so I felt safer. My first stop was customs. When the customs agent read my passport, he looked up at me and said "Bienvenue Monsieur duRosier." He assumed I spoke French and he said something to the effect of, "You are Guy's son, yes?" I nodded politely and he ushered me through customs far more quickly than any of the other passengers ahead of me. Outside of customs I saw Guy waving to me from his car. There was another gentleman standing beside him who had the look of family. I presumed he was family. As soon as I attempted to cross the street to the car, I was descended upon by a horde of young beggars. They were speaking what I sensed was Creole and they had their hands out. As I neared the car, Guy met me and gave me a big hug. Then he shooed the beggars away with a vitriolic criticism that left them scattering like pigeons.

Guy hugged me exuberantly while his nephew Phillipe looked on. "Robaire, this is your cousin Phillipe Guillaume." I knew that he was family even from a distance. It was a remarkable feeling to see a resemblance in another face besides Guy's.

Phillipe extended his hand to me and said, "It's like looking at my uncle thirty years ago. Welcome to Haiti, Robaire."

I thanked Phillipe and ducked into the car. The drive to Guy's home in Petionville was beautiful. The duRosier home was located far up in the hills where the air was cooler and the bougainvillea trees grew in abundance. I half expected a zombie to walk in front of the car or to see a voodoo ceremony on the side of the road. But my suspicions about this little mysterious island were quickly laid to rest as we circled up into a beautiful neighborhood of luxurious three story homes. Most of the homes were white stucco with columns in front. The architecture was very French. And up here in Petionville every one of the homes had a spectacular sweeping view of the azure waters of the Caribbean. Before pulling into the driveway, Guy told me about my cousin Phillipe, who was behind the wheel.

"Philippe is one of the top orthopedic surgeons in all of Haiti."

Phillippe added, "I practice in New York about half of the year, and I teach here at the university."

His English was polished. I wished that every American could see what I was seeing. This was not what they would have come to expect of Haiti. Ignorant Americans assumed it was an island full of people with AIDS, trying to build little boats to float across the sea to Miami. Boat people and AIDS. That was likely one of the first things to come to mind, and why? Because of the horrible propaganda machine. Haitians were one of the only immigrant groups who were consistently turned away by the United States. Not even the Cubans were treated so harshly. It doesn't take a rocket scientist to understand why. Color. That tricky little epidermis coming into play again. I was sitting in a car with two Haitians, one of whom played to a sold-out Carnegie Hall and received rave reviews from the New York Times; the other, a highly regarded surgeon. And to top it off, they were my people. I loved it!

The front door opened and out stepped several people to greet me. The first was Guy's sister, my Aunt Giselle. She was most definitely a duRosier. Then first and second cousins and friends of Guy's.

Aunt Giselle spoke no English at all but said to me nonetheless, "Bon forme, Robaire," as she hugged me and looked at me from head to toe. Guy translated without my having to ask him, "She says you have good form Robaire."

I said thank you to her, "Merci tante-tante." Guy had taught me some affectionate things to say ahead of time. 'Tante-tante' was an affection-ate way of saying 'Auntie.'

The person that I was eager to meet was upstairs in the biggest bed-room of the house. It was like there was a familial hierarchy inside of this large house. And the higher up you went, the more elder the family member.

I reached into my bag to find the mint Frangos that Marianne, in her uniquely thoughtful way, had sent with me specifically to deliver to Grandmother Francine. Guy saw the Frangos and licked his lips.

"My wife, my Anne-Marie is so thoughtful. How I love your mother, Robaire. Class!" Guy said the word class and his face was so animated. He dragged out the word while he squinted with his eyes to punctuate his emotion. He gauged every word, and every action for its effect. He was like the superior court judge presiding over etiquette. Marianne's unexpected gift for his mother practically elevated her to nobility status in his eyes. "What a wooo-man," he sang in a high voice.

We made our way up the final flight of marble steps and turned right to go down the hallway to Mama Francine's room. I followed closely behind Guy, timidly. I wasn't sure how many more times my heart could take the thrill of these life-defining moments. We moved into her room and there she sat in her rocking chair, fanning herself and rocking back and forth. Guy bent down and kissed her on the cheek, and then he moved aside so that she could see me. She reached for her glasses, put them on and looked up at me. I bent down to hug and kiss her. We were the exact same color. Her father was French with the surname, Petrus, and her mother was black. Her nose and her eyes were the traits that most obviously had passed through to my generation. She was dressed in a beautiful summer dress. She looked like she was going to Sunday church. As I backed away from her, she clasped her hands together and proclaimed something in the most beautiful French that even wowed Guy. He fell backwards onto her bed in a display of emotion at what she had just said about me. I looked back and forth between my grandmother and my father and pleaded to know what was being said. Guy sat upright, regained his composure, and with a big smile on his face said, "Robaire, your Mama Francine just said that meeting you today, and seeing what a fine young man you are, is like a warm blanket in the winter of her life."

I gasped at the beauty of her statement. I could see where Guy got his lyricism from. She was indeed in the winter of her life. She was ninety-three years old and she regarded me as a warm blanket in the winter of her life. It was the most beautiful use of a metaphor I had ever heard in my entire life.

I reached down to hug her again and told her, "Je t'aime Mama

Francine. Je t'aime beau-coup." She wiped tears away from the corners of her eyes. I gave her the Frangos that Marianne had sent for her, and she tasted one. She was in heaven. She loved those chocolates so much that she ordered Guy to lock them in the refrigerator. I laughed at that but she was serious. Guy explained to me that the house had a staff of cooks and maids, and that Mama Francine suspected the chocolates would disappear if left unattended. She was dogmatic about it as she pointed Guy towards her little refrigerator outside in the hall. She barked some command at him in French and Guy obeyed, "Yes, Mamie."

We ate our lunch in Mama Francine's room. It was my second Haitian meal, the first coming in the Bahamas when I had first met Guy. The meal was delivered by the staff. She set up tables for us to eat on and set silverware for each of us. It was very odd to be served by this Haitian woman. But Guy explained to me that it was the best job that they could ever hope to have. They were compensated well considering they were uneducated. The fried plantains were my favorite. They were delicious, sweet, fried bananas. I had never tasted them before. After the meal, everyone drank coffee from these tiny little cups. I understood after a few sips why the coffee was served in such small cups. It was seriously strong. And good. Coffee was one of the major exports in Haiti since the days of colonization. Guy raved about the Haitian coffee. As we sat and drank our coffee, we moved out onto the veranda outside of Mama Francine's room. From there one could look west out over the beautiful bougainvillea trees to the ocean. I was exactly where I belonged at that moment. I remember thinking to myself that a man's heart can be healed.

One of Guy's very close friends came out from his room where he was watching Brazil challenge Croatia in soccer's World Cup. His name was Fa-Fa. He looked like Gandhi. He only recently had returned to Haiti from Africa where he was working for the United Nations as an interpreter. He and Guy proceeded to dive into an intellectual conversation, in English for my benefit. The conversation would have made any coffee house or café in Paris proud. They talked about everything from astronomy, physics, politics, to music. Guy asked Fa-Fa's advice on a title for our compact disc we were recording. Fa-Fa said, "How about, Guy duRosier Revisitee?" Guy liked the idea of it. Then the conversation shifted to Copernicus, Freud, Einstein, Plato. These men were intellectuals in the purest sense. They took great pleasure in bantering back and forth, sizing each other's intellect up like a prizefighter throwing a jab, then counterpunching with an uppercut. However, in this case, the sport was I. Q. I kept my mouth closed and listened, knowing that my time would come when someone would ask me something and I would have the floor. Then I would lay some words on them, words that always came naturally and effortlessly to me in speech, and they would know that I was their equal.

The heat and all of the excitement served to tire me out and Guy noticed. "Robaire, let me show you your room. You can take a nap and later we'll go out." Guy showed me to my room and stayed with me so that we could talk.

I said, "Mama Francine is elegant. I noticed a Scrabble board on her desk. Who does she play with?"

Guy answered, "She plays against herself. So that she can keep her mind lucid. She is a true wordsmith, Robaire."

I remarked, "That is sweet how she keeps the photograph of Grandfather Andre directly in front of her rocking chair. She must really have loved him."

"Yes, Robaire, she never even thought of remarrying. It has been fifty years since he died."

Guy could see that I was dozing off, so he said, "Rest your eyes now, Robaire."

The ceiling fan overhead whirled around and around, fanning me comfortably. Never before had I experienced such vivid imagery in my dreams. A tall thin man was standing at the altar in tuxedo and top hat, and standing beside him was a tiny woman in her wedding gown. The disparity in height was hilarious. I woke up laughing hysterically.

Guy looked at me and shook his head back and forth, commenting, "You must teach me this strange ability to laugh in your sleep."

"Papa, I can't explain it. I never do that. It must be something in the air here." I leaned over to look at him and my cheek hit something on my pillow. The pillow smelled wonderful. I looked at it and oddly there was a bouquet of orchids lying beside me on my pillowcase. I gave Guy a perplexed look, and he motioned with his head over to the corner of the room.

There sat the most beautiful little girl in her Catholic grade-school uniform. Her skin was the color of caramel, similar to Guy's. She looked to be about seven years old. She smiled at me and introduced herself, "Bon jour Robaire, je m'appelle Babette." Then she switched to English, "Do you like your flowers?"

I was amazed at the grace of this child, "Yes, thank you very much Babette, that was so sweet of you."

She giggled and ran out of the room. "That is your cousin Babette. She was upstairs having her after school study session with Mama Francine, and I suspect Mama Francine put her up to the flower idea."

I marveled, "Papa, Haitians are too much."

A child setting a bouquet of hand-picked flowers on my pillow while I slept. There was a simple beauty in those words that could never do them justice. I looked once more at the flowers, then at Guy, and considered that to be one of the most beautiful moments of my life, to date. The purity of a child's intentions magnified the experience.

That evening, Guy had a big surprise in store for me. Cousin Philippe drove us to a club called 'Café des Arts' in Petionville, which was just a few miles up from Port au Prince.

"Robaire," Philippe called, "Look at the marquee."

There was Guy's name in bright lights. We walked inside and everyone immediately crowded Guy with handshakes and pats on the shoulder. Everybody called him "Maestro." The people just loved him. On stage was a young man playing the tenor saxophone. He was making a valiant effort at some improvisational jazz, but it was not professional.

I sat beside Guy and told him, "Papa, you blow that Guy out of the water on your worst day."

He immediately shushed me scornfully. "Robaire, you don't have to say that, we'll let my 'axe' speak for itself." When he started calling his saxophone his 'axe,' then I knew he was getting juiced up to perform. As the young man's set was winding down, Guy leaned over to whisper in my ear, "The Haitian people don't know that I play the sax, wait until they see this."

"How could they not know?"

"I always play the piano, or conduct in live shows here."

When Guy took the stage there was a roar from the crowd. He took out a new reed and fit it onto his mouthpiece while his accompaniment tuned up their instruments. I had seen Guy perform live in Nassau, however that was only in front of about fifty people. This was much different. There were upwards of one thousand people at this venue. Guy knew that I idolized John Coltrane, so he opened his set with a cut from Coltrane's "A Love Supreme," recording. He was wailing on that sax. I mean really tearing it up, and I was freaking out. He was the shyest guy in the room off-stage but when the lights went down and he took the stage, he was transformed into something entirely different. He joked and played with the audience in French in between songs. He even danced! And he danced with a flair that only a black man has. My father was really, really, cool.

Our table was filled with interesting people. There was a woman who sang opera in Haiti's St. Trinite Philharmonic, and a second cousin who was an actress, and beside me sat a friend of Guy's who was a journalist for Haiti's newspaper. He and I began chatting in between sets. I asked him what it was like to be a journalist under the stifling, twenty-eight-year dictatorship of the Duvaliers. His answer was chilling.

He told me that there was no such thing as freedom of speech during the dictatorship, and that to dissent was not an option. "One night after I had written an article about the ton-ton macoutes, Duvalier's secret militia, and their suspected role in the disappearance of a prominent Haitian businessman, I was taken against my will to an abandoned dump area outside of Port au Prince. I was blindfolded and lined up against a wall as if to be executed. They even went as far as to fire their rifles at me, but to my surprise I was not hit. Fortunately, they were only sending me a message. They left me there blindfolded and hand-cuffed to find my way back."

To hear this story against the backdrop of my father's music in a beautiful, artistic environment was surreal. It defined Haiti, in a way. Bi-polar emotions that were never, ever far from one another in this country.

Guy was finishing up his set with a classic number from Miles Davis' 'Sketches of Spain.' The breathtaking music pouring forth from Guy's horn, contrasted by the horrifying story by the journalist, made my head spin. This was a mystical little island indeed.

To say that Guy was like the proverbial big fish in a small pond didn't even begin to capture his appeal in Haiti. It was more like he was a five-carat diamond in a coin purse. He sauntered off stage looking dapper in his jazz-appropriate attire consisting of gray slacks with a navy blazer, crisp white shirt, and tie. All around the club came shouts of "Bravo Maestro, bravo. Encore, encore." Guy bowed politely as he made his way to the table.

"Well my son, did we kill them?"

All I did was shake my head back and forth at him in disbelief. I wasn't going to be surprised at anything he did on stage ever again.

"I saw you conversing with my friend Jean Michel, the editor of our paper, the Haiti Observateur. I purposely sat him beside you knowing that two writers would have plenty to discuss."

"Papa, he is amazing. He told me about nearly being executed by the Ton-ton Macoutes."

"Robaire, Haiti is a country of auditory and optical surveillance." I could tell he was doing his best to translate from French to English to accommodate me. And it was obvious that when he spoke French, it was at the highest of proficiency.

I wondered to myself, mildly amused, at what he would have thought of the Ebonics movement that was gaining momentum in Oakland, California. He would have scoffed, eyebrows lowered over squinting eyes, and admonished the very idea like he scolded the beggars at the airport.

Guy quickly added, "The Ton-ton Macoutes were Duvalier's feared henchmen who came swiftly in the night and murdered men, women and children indiscriminately."

I understood why he left his beloved country for nearly two decades, choosing to tour places like Europe, Asia, and Canada.

We returned home and I paced quickly up the stairs to say goodnight to Mama Francine. She sat regally in her rocking chair fanning herself and playing Scrabble against herself, quite a formidable opponent. Her entire demeanor changed quickly when Guy and I entered the room as the corners of her mouth turned up in a wonderful smile.

It was obvious to me after just two days in Haiti that Guy was Mama Francine's favorite child. And she was treated reverentially by Guy in return. I noticed a ritual when entering the 'Queen's' room, it required bending down on one knee so that she didn't have to get up out of her rocking chair. First she would kiss one cheek, then the other, and then hold our heads in her hands as she placed a third and final kiss on our foreheads.

She requested coffee and ice cream from the staff so that we could sit down and tell her everything about the evening in complete detail. She was no longer able to get around much without tiring, so her room became the storytelling sanctuary. It was really something to behold to see everyone gathering in her room to regale her with the evening's events. And the story- telling was almost more enjoyable than being there because the events were delivered with so much animation, allowing Mama Francine to fill in the gaps vividly based upon the retelling. I compared it to enjoying a fantastic book then going to the movie and being a bit let down. She was being read to by a room full of duRosiers who could deliver a story with incomparable color. Each person took their turn, with Guy usually having the floor for the majority of the story. And he would make her laugh without fail, like the court jester sent in to entertain the queen.

I was witnessing what in my opinion amounted to a lost art in my country, but was alive and well in this beleaguered island nation. It was called families gathering and talking with each other on a regular basis. Nobody went straight for the television in this home. The human relationship was respected here, and more impressive still was the fact that everyone from adult to child showed reverence for the elder of that home, Mama Francine. Even though I was only two days into my relationship with Mama Francine, she asked Guy to have me tell my version of the evening's events to her. It was almost as if she wanted to hear everybody's version and then disseminate for herself, and patch together the best pieces of each person's version. She also was able to ascertain each individual's personality shining through in a unique way.

When I finished telling my version, she said something to Guy that was impassioned in its delivery, and Guy recounted to me, "Robaire, she says that she appreciates your sensitivity and especially your candor. And that your sincerity of expression touches her heart." I realized that I would have loved growing up in this house around these people. Mama Francine saw everyone's unique strength and made sure to compliment it.

We were always the last ones to leave the room and Guy would have stayed talking with his mother all night if she could have remained awake. I hated leaving her room every single time it came time to go downstairs because something inside of me knew that these conversations over the course of my two week visit would be the only chance I would have to know my grandmother. So it was that I turned and followed Guy out of Mama Francine's room slowly, like an enlisted man forced to leave his family to go to war. There was no hurry in my step, no rush to leave that magnificent woman, my Mama Francine.

Patrick Audant extended his hand to shake mine, and said in very proficient English, "Welcome to my recording studio, Robaire." His English was better than most of the Haitians I had met thus far and he had traveled back and forth between Haiti and New York to find the best recording equipment he could buy. His studio was regarded as the best in Haiti, but you would never guess it from sheer appearances. His studio was in his home, and the key to his success was in the acoustics of the room. It was small, but the hardwood floors and high ceilings gave it a fabulous sound, combined with his state-of-the-art microphones.

"How would you like to hear what your father and I have laid down thus far?"

I shifted in my chair, "Yeah, lay it on me."

"You are going to love this first track. We had the Philharmonic of Haiti in last week to record with your father and it is in my opinion the best work Guy has ever done."

I knew that was saying a lot considering he had recorded over thirty-six albums since 1948. He clicked a series of buttons and out came the masterpiece. I knew after hearing two bars that it was the finest sound he had yet to record. I hadn't heard every one of Guy's recordings, but most of them. I heard what sounded like a room full of violinists, then I heard Guy's unmistakable signature on the piano.

Guy shouted over the music that was playing at a very loud decibel, "This song has a total of twenty- four separate tracks Robaire. Listen closely and you'll hear all kinds of things."

I could make out a triangle, an oboe, a french horn, several saxophones, both soprano and tenor, congas, viola, a choir, and on and on. I kept to my promise that I had made one night before at the live concert where I said I would never be surprised by anything he did musically, ever again. I just looked at Guy and smiled. Then he came as close to bragging as I had ever heard. Bragging just would not be acceptable to a man of his stature, however, so he masked his pride in a brilliant disguise that anyone besides his son would not have noticed.

"I am not, nor have I ever been afraid of Quincy Jones," Guy said with chin raised.

One thing was apparent, and that was that the St. Trinite Philharmonic was the best accompaniment Guy had ever had on a recording. The sound was perfect. Guy said with pride, "Robaire, did you think that we could get sound like this from this little room, on this little Third World island?"

"Nothing about you, or Haiti, surprises me, Papa."

When we came to the third track, Guy motioned me over toward the stand-up microphone. He was so at-home in the studio, and it was fun to see him completely in his element.

"It's your time to record Do-do, Ti-ti, Robaire. Just sing it the way we have practiced over and over, and if you make a mistake with the French, we can simply back up and record it again. Sing with emotion and remember to breathe, but stay about six inches away from the microphone."

I should have been nervous, but I wasn't at all considering I was just hanging out with my father, my best friend, my soul-mate. Patrick put his headphones on and told me to do the same.

I could hear him talking to me inside of the headphones saying, "Okay Robaire, on three you will hear the instrumentation, and just begin to sing when it gets to your part."

I gave him the thumbs up and Guy stood in the corner of the room looking at me very seriously, as he was all business in a recording studio. Having had over a month of practice, I could have sung this song in my sleep, but I wasn't prepared for the beauty of the instrumentation that Guy put to it. It was simply beautiful, lovely. The sound gave me the impression of a pendulum, with a back and forth, lullaby feel. I began to sing my part with all of the sensitivity and emotion that I could muster. I closed my eyes as I sang with the intent of honoring my father, my mother, Mama Francine, and all of the duRosiers' past, present and future. When I was finished, I opened my eyes and looked at Guy for approval. He gave me a big smile and asked Patrick to play it back for me.

Hearing your own voice can be very disconcerting, as it just never sounds the way that you think it does, but I was very happy with what I heard. So were Guy and Patrick. Guy said to me, "Robaire, I think your new nickname should be 'one-take' because you knocked it out on your very first take. We will preview this recording tonight for our harshest critics, the duRosier family. If Mama Francine, Giselle, Phillippe, and Fa-Fa like it, then and only then is it ready for the marketplace."

We all gathered around the stereo system on the main floor to listen to what Guy had poured his heart and soul into for the last year. Mama

Francine even came downstairs with the assistance of Tante Giselle.

Cousin Phillippe put the disc into the player and then came the most remarkable fifty-five minutes of uninterrupted music.

It was odd to have so many people in one room and not one person speaking from start to finish. The room was full of pure connoisseurs of music and I was nervous as could be.

The first response came from the corner of the room from Guy's dear friend Fa-Fa, the man who looked like Gandhi and worked for the United Nations in Africa. Fa-Fa sniffled ever so softly then reached into his pocket for a handkerchief to blow his nose. Guy stood and walked over near his lifelong friend with whom he had so much in common and put his right arm around Fa-Fa's shoulder. I could now see the tears that had trailed down both cheeks and left a sheen on his face. When Fa-Fa regained his composure, he summed up the recording succinctly using just four words to critique Guy's work.

"It's something like nirvana."

I couldn't argue with that. After all, it was like an ideal condition of harmony, stability, and joy, and Fa-Fa's assessment of the music cemented my theory that all Haitians were born poets. Everything that these people said was dramatic, lyrical, or poetic. Poetry must have been part of the educational orientation in Haiti, much like phonics was in the United States.

The critique was universally positive, leaving Guy first relieved, then exhilarated.

At nearly four in the afternoon, suddenly all of the power in the house went out. It was the second time in three days that the power went dead, but the house had a powerful generator that would quickly boot up the power and most importantly kick the air conditioning back on. It was really hot and I noticed that without even lying out in the sun I was getting browner and browner every day, just from walking around with Guy. In fact, after just three days, I was probably darker than I had ever been before, approaching Guy's caramel coloring. The momentary loss of power surprised nobody but me, so Guy simply smiled at me and said, "Third World."

As the power returned to normal, Guy and the others spoke to each other in excited tones, then when they were finished, Guy, as usual, began translating for me.

"Robaire, tonight the best female 'chanteuse' will be performing at the Port au Prince opera house. She'll be on stage with the members of the philharmonic who performed on our compact disc. Would you like to go?"

Quickly, I answered, "Yeah."

A suit and tie was a must for the occasion, but I knew I was going to be burning up in the oppressive heat. Haiti was hot! And it just seemed like the sun was closer, almost like it was asking me for a piggy-back ride. Its proximity to the equator was the reason, and I began to hardly recognize myself in the mirror when I peered at it. Seattle was the northernmost city in the United States, bordering Canada, and it was possible to get a tan, but not much of one. Now I was like a chameleon, changing colors dramatically by the hour. I prayed for air conditioning in this theater we were going to.

Papa, as usual, stopped upstairs to say goodbye to Mama Francine and tried valiantly to coax her out for the evening, knowing that she would not, and could not really go.

He said to me, "The fact that she cannot physically go does not preclude me from always inviting her. Her body may not attend, but her spirit may take me up on the offer." This was a son that adored his mother and it was a wonderful thing to see.

Guy and I entered her room and he sat at the edge of the bed while she rocked back and forth in her chair with her beautiful dress on while pearls adorned her neck.

I kneeled at Guy's side and Mama Francine looked at us both from head to toe, then stated assuredly as usual, "Robaire is the philosophical stone, kneeling at the foot of the author of his life." With that, she turned her head and played her next move against herself in her ongoing game of Scrabble.

Walking down the staircase I said to Guy, "Papa, I am in love with that woman. Everything she says is utterly profound and I don't know how I am possibly going to say goodbye to her next week."

"She is an intellectual, make no mistake Robaire."

He emphasized the word intellectual for effect. He slowly stated each syllable. "An in-tell-ect-u-al." He stopped walking as he said it and held onto my shoulder giving me a piercing look with one eye squinted a bit smaller than the other. He meant for me to understand fully what she meant to our heritage, and to the heritage of any duRosiers to come in the future.

There was only one route to the opera house, and as diligently as Guy tried to protect me from the 'other' side of Haiti, I saw what could only be described as horrifying, shocking poverty along the waterfront in the notorious 'Cite Soleil' slums. Here again was the happy and sad face of theater. To the west, I saw a cathedral that would have been proud to stand in any city. It was blindingly white, with huge columns in the front and an unbelievably large gold cross on the top of the structure. I had seen this magnificent church on final descent into Port au Prince from about ten thousand feet in the air. But to the east, was a different vision. It was a vision of squalor. I could only think of the African bush about one hundred years ago. People were actually walking around naked, and I saw little lean- to huts in the mud that served as homes to these people. Two pieces of aluminum leaned one against the other serving as shelter. And groups of six to eight people huddling around them, smoking pipes, men and women. All of this was just thirty yards or so from the main road we were driving on. Guy noticed that I saw all of this and he didn't like it at all. 'Cite Soleil,' was the 'bad uncle' that nobody talked about and the family hoped he never came to family functions.

Guy said, "These are the exiled President Aristide's people. Don't be fooled by appearances, because we are targets to them. They would take our land, all of our possessions, and necklace us in a second. Meanwhile, Clinton protects Aristide, the champion of the unwashed, like a step-son."

There it was, my political science master's course. I knew we would talk about the politics of Haiti at some point during my stay. I couldn't hope to understand the situation intimately because this was a nation which never knew democracy. It was the classic case of the haves verses the have nots. So while I empathized with the poverty I was witnessing, I understood Guy's contempt for it as well. More than anything I was fascinated at seeing a country without a middle class. It was missing altogether. People were either very wealthy or unbelievably poor. Nothing was going to change that, short of the ominous system to the south in Cuba. Communism. But the United States would never let that happen. The twenty-six year U. S. occupation couldn't change things so I reduced it to an interesting theoretical study of class struggle.

I was happy to be out of the slum and parking next to a beautiful building in downtown Port au Prince. Still, I knew I'd never forget what I saw because the depravity was incomparable. I had traveled extensively throughout Mexico and had seen children selling Chiclets for family meal money, but the slums of Cite Soleil made the worst conditions in Mexico look like middle class living.

The storytelling session was back in full swing in Mama Francine's room even though it was close to midnight. Guy raved about the string section and Mama Francine interrupted him to say something that had the whole room laughing. Guy was laughing too hard to interpret for me so Tante Giselle relayed her reply to me saying, "She said, can black people really play the violin?"

Mama Francine's self deprecating humor had brought the house down with riotous laughter, and I joined into the mix late. Papa was still laughing so hard that he was curled up into a ball and kicking one leg into the air with abandon. I just wished that I could have recognized the humor first-hand in French so that nothing would be lost in the translation.

Out on the veranda, Fa-Fa stood like a sentry, waiting to engage anyone in conversation who would join him, however he never joined in the group in Mama Francine's room. Instead, he preferred to shyly wait in the wings for conversation to come to him, so I excused myself to go speak with this gentle, Ghandi look alike.

Fa-Fa appreciated my company and took the opportunity to tell me something astounding about Guy. "Robaire, your father would never tell you this about himself, but I believe it is vital for you to know nonetheless. Days before 'Papa Doc, Francois Duvalier, died, he invited three people to come to Haiti to receive the honor of 'The Knight of the Grand Crois, Geneva Switzerland'. This honor bestowed upon its recipient, knighthood status with Geneva. Let me tell you who the three honorees were, Robaire. They were Muhammad Ali, Pele, and Guy duRosier, your precious father. Your papa is a national treasure in our country, an icon whose legacy will most certainly be the rehabilitation of Haitian music for generations to come."

I questioned Fa-Fa, "How come he is so secretive? He never talks about himself."

"It wouldn't be proper for him to tell you these things, yet in my opinion, you deserve to know, you must know."

I took a deep breath and smelled the bougainvillea trees while I looked overhead at stars that never, ever seemed so close. I could almost reach up and grab one, it seemed. I wasn't sure what the optical illusion was, or if it was Haiti playing tricks on me, but those stars were unusually close to the ground. One of them must have fallen on my father years and years ago, sprinkling him with stardust and promising a life of enchantment in exchange for a song.

The day had come for me to leave the magic island, and I was not at all eager to go. I made Guy promise to take me by the art gallery on my way to the airport because I had brought some extra money just for paintings. The Haitians were known for their exquisite art that had an impressionistic influence but differed in their use of the vibrant, primary colors.

Before leaving the house, though, came the task of having to say goodbye to the family. It was difficult, but nothing compared to my last goodbye that I had to go upstairs and down the hall to Mama Francine's room for. She was waiting for me as usual in her prettiest dress. She had a handkerchief in her hand that she had already been using according to the evidence from her puffy, watery eyes. I knelt down to hug her and I couldn't let go for the longest time. I kept whispering in her ear, "Je t'aime beaucoup Mama Francine." She was ninety-three years old and we both seemed to know that this was goodbye forever, so I asked Guy to translate for me and told her, "I will always try to make you proud of me and any future duRosiers will do the same, I promise you that."

She had her rosary in one hand and patted my cheek with the other. Then she kissed me on both cheeks and my forehead. I was so overcome with conflicting emotions that I almost got sick. I was grateful for even knowing her, but I could have used about ten more years of her wisdom and her tenderness. I squeezed her tan-colored right hand into my own and could not tell the difference between our skin color. I took one last glance around her room, it was the room of a sweet, elegant, poetic woman adorned with the trappings of class. I took a snapshot for my mind never to forget, then I tried to force a smile to come to my lips, looked directly into my grandmother's eyes and let the words that were impossible to speak pass from my heart to hers. I turned and walked downstairs where Guy was waiting for me outside. It was the only time he did not accompany me to Mama Francine's room. Instead, he gave me a wonderful moment alone with my lovely grandmother.

When he saw me he immediately came to my side and said, "Robaire, are you all right?" "You look green." Having to say goodbye to her made me physically ill.

"Papa, I'll be fine. I just didn't realize how hard it would be for me to say goodbye to Mama Francine."

He knew. He put his large right hand on my shoulder while I looked out the car window as we drove away. He allowed me the dignity to let a man regain his composure in the company of other men.

We stopped at the Issa El Saieh gallery in Port au Prince on our way to the airport, just as Guy had promised me all along. Issa was a Syrian man who had migrated to Haiti in the early forties and originally put together one of the finest bands that Haiti has known since. Naturally, Guy was the headliner for Issa's band so when they saw each other on the first floor of his gallery, Issa El Saieh let out a boisterous greeting in French that had Papa smiling. Right away, he barked at someone to bring us coffee, and it was in our hands within minutes. Issa was quite a famous character in Haiti, made so by Graham Green's famous novel, *The Comedians*. Graham Green wrote about Issa in the book but changed his name to protect him. Duvalier, the feared dictator, did not like foreigners in his country, especially wealthy foreigners, because they were a threat to his totalitarian regime. Thus, Issa El Saieh was a marked man. The word got back to him that the Ton ton Macoutes, Duvaliers secret militia, were coming for him. Issa was one of the lucky ones because he fled Haiti and did not return for nearly ten years. The paranoia had subsided by that time, and Issa El Saieh quit the music business and started to buy and sell Haitian art. Every prominent Haitian I had met was forced to leave their beloved country at some point in time during Francois Duvalier's reign. They called it the Haitian diaspora. I wandered among the paintings while Guy and Issa reminisced about music. Then I spotted the most magnificent painting, but just as I was looking at it, Issa shouted at me, "Get your hands out of your father's wallet." That was his way of telling me it was too expensive. It turned out to be over twenty thousand dollars.

I told him how much I had to spend and he quickly ushered me to a different section of the gallery. I still found five great paintings and he had someone wrap them up for me.

The drive to the airport was only about ten minutes from Issa's gallery, and Guy took the opportunity to tell me that he would finish the recording in a couple of weeks, then come to Seattle to be reunited with his 'wife' Anne-Marie.

"Tell your beautiful mother that Papa Guy misses her immensely."

"I will, Papa."

I hugged Guy and thanked him for everything, then with my paintings in one hand and my suitcase in the other, I breezed through the airport terminal to my boarding gate. The American Airlines 757 aircraft stood parked outside with a portable staircase leading up to the interior. I walked up the stairs and felt the burning sun stinging the nape of my neck. After two weeks of that sun, I now looked far more Haitian than I did when I arrived. I hoped that the flight attendant would let me board with my paintings since they were very fragile and very expensive. She did. I found my seat and listened to the French and Creole that was being spoken all around me. It served to remind me of this wonderful island that I was now leaving, and the most vivid memories that I would take back to Seattle with me were of the extremes. It was an extremely fun, poetic, beautiful place, but at the same time it was extremely poor, isolated, and dangerous. In the country where my grandmother could be so tender and sweet, you could also be made into a zombie for being accused of stealing property. Nobody went to the police in Haiti for justice. No, they went to the local houngan or mambo, the high priest and priestess of voodoo. And these spiritual gurus meted out justice of another sort altogether as in burying the accused alive and making zombies of them. Indeed, the majority of Haitians feared this far more than any jail term. Even the educated, bourgeois Haitians did not ignore voodoo and its power. They simply were not as overt in their practice of it. Yes, this place, this mysterious little place that I was leaving would stay with me forever. The smell of it and the feel of it were now in my bones.

I closed my eyes as we were now quickly gaining speed for take off, and held to one vision of Haiti that would come to personify my stay and my impression of the island. A bouquet of red, pink, and yellow flowers lying on my pillow right beside my head, and a little eight-year-old girl sitting in the corner of the room waiting for me to notice, then smiling at me and shyly running out of the room.

In Haiti, all things moved in constant half- embrace, the desired and the dreaded, the repugnant and the cherished, the pursued and that which you would escape. These things moved within Haiti as lights and shadows in pairs that cling.

Part IV

THE ELIXIR OF LIFE

"Love, is not love which alters where it alteration finds, or bends with the remover to remove; No, it is an ever fixed mark that looks into the eye of the tempest and is not shaken."

WILLIAM SHAKESPEARE

12

LOVE

MARIANNE hardly recognized me when I stepped inside of the apartment.

"Robert, you're black!"

"Yeah Mom, and don't forget beautiful."

She laughed at me and asked me if I was fishing. Whenever I needed a compliment I fished for it from her and she always recognized what I was getting at. I moved into the kitchen to get something to eat, hungry after the long, long flight from Miami to Seattle. The lighting in the kitchen was very bright, so Marianne got a closer look at me and moved over to put her leg beside mine so we could compare color.

"You're as dark as I've ever seen you. You're as dark as your father," she replied.

"Mom," I said, "There is something about the sun in Haiti, I'm telling you it is closer, like it's right on top of you. And it's the same with the stars. They seem so incredibly close you could almost reach out and touch one. I think I saw two or three shooting stars every night out on the veranda, and each time we'd see one, Papa would remark that someone's lover was dying. It is Haitian folklore that a shooting star signifies a soul in transition."

Marianne was listening, but she listened like a child at an opera. She wanted to cut to the chase. She wanted her man back inside of her arms, and she wanted it now.

"When is your father coming back here?" she asked.

"Well first, Mom before I forget, you were a huge hit with Mama Francine and the Frango's. She freaked out over those chocolates. She liked them so much that she had Papa lock them up in the freezer so the staff couldn't steal them. I mean I actually saw a padlock on that freezer, Mom."

Marianne laughed and laughed the way only she could. When she laughed it wasn't half-hearted. No, she laughed herself to tears and I loved that about her. She made me feel about ten years younger every time she laughed.

I continued, "Now on to the important stuff. Papa asked me to tell you that he misses his wife, his Anne-Marie, immensely. And he really emphasized 'immensely'."

Marianne, like a prosecutor cross-examining her witness, went right back for the kill.

"Robert, I asked you, when is your father coming back to Seattle?"

"Well Mama," I hedged, "He has to wrap up the recording and that will take him about two more weeks. Then he may have to return to Nassau to work."

Marianne's wheels began spinning and I could see her mind working like a computer. "Will you please put in for tickets to The Bahamas for me tomorrow at your pass bureau, Robert, so that I can go see your father?"

"Absolutely Mama, you've got it." If there was one thing I knew about that crazy emotion called love, it was that without it you could laugh, but not all of your laughter, and weep, but not all of your tears. I also knew that love could teach us the pain of too much tenderness, a pain that sickened me having to say goodbye to Mama Francine. But the thing I understood the most about love was that you can't direct the course of love, for love, if it finds you worthy, directs your course.

Marianne and Guy fit this definition to a tee. Her life was changing course dramatically and the beauty of it was that she was letting it happen. She was riding this wave like a champion surfer and the next stop was The Bahamas. Her initiative and her courage were awe-inspiring. It was a testimony to her love for Guy, and I thought it was shaping up to be the most wonderful love story I had ever seen, heard of, read about, or watched at any theater.

Guy and Marianne were two adults who had lived already full lives, so their passion was not without reason. And at the same time, their reason was not confining. When passion can live through its own flame and rise above its own ashes, then the way has been paved for a love supreme. My mother and father's love for each other was unfolding like a lotus of countless petals.

147

It had been a few months since Guy and Marianne were together but they each recognized that love grows stronger when there are spaces in the togetherness. Guy was very patient, yet Marianne was less so. She took the first opportunity to go to The Bahamas to see him. I wanted to go with her, but I also had to get back to work after all of the time I had taken off to go to Haiti. I also recognized that my mother and father needed time alone together. The thought of it thrilled me, but I still had not allowed myself to believe that it could become a permanent situation. I could see very clearly that they were in love, but I did not trust it. There were remnants of the warrior's mentality from my childhood that would be difficult to let go of now, if ever at all. I was so comfortable with expecting the worst of any situation so that I could steel my mind with determination to deal with adversity. It would take an unbelievable leap of faith for me to ever trust love, but I was taking baby steps in that very direction.

I hugged Marianne tightly as usual and told her how much I loved her. "I will miss you, Mom," I said as I kissed her on both cheeks, adopting my Haitian family's custom.

"I'll miss you too, Robert. But we'll call you tonight to let you know that I got there."

"Okay Mama, you go and have a great time with Papa, and please say hi to him for me."

"I will, Robert. I am so excited to see your father. I just love him so much." She was glowing, the way that only she could.

I watched her walk through the doors and into the terminal with wonder at how she could feel so confident traveling thousands of miles, yet she would not drive into the city if her life depended on it. The way she toted the rolling suitcase I got her made me proud. She had that confident airport walk like a flight attendant, which assured me she would be just fine. I knew that for Marianne to travel alone to another country, switching airplanes twice and going through customs, she must really, really love my father. This was the same woman who took one route and one route only to get to work. She sometimes lost her car in grocery store parking lots. Love was in the air.

Marianne collected her luggage at baggage claim, then turned to see her lover waiting for her outside. She marveled at how much Guy had changed in the three months they had been apart. It was as if he had undergone a transformation. He looked younger, thinner in the face and overall just happier. She wondered if she had been the catalyst behind his metamorphosis. She didn't realize it but she had been through the same change. She had lost about ten pounds and she looked fantastic too.

When she reached Guy, he reached out to hug her and said, "You see the face Marianne, you have composed me!" She took both of his cheeks in her hands and pulled him close enough so she could kiss him. She gave him a big, wet kiss right there in the Nassau airport.

"Mamie, these Bahamians will think we are teen-agers the way we are kissing, and it will have proved our son, Robaire, correct."

He was referring to the time I told them that they looked like teen-agers in love. Guy absolutely loved it when I said that. He had told me that in one of his conversations on the phone with Marianne he remarked how handsome I was, and that maybe they should have another child together. He paused to see my surprise then said, "Robaire, all I heard was a lot of screaming on the other end of the phone." I laughed.

Marianne continued kissing him, saying, "Let them think whatever they want." She added as they walked to the car, "Our first separation was thirty years, and our second was three months, that's an improvement, but I don't even like being away from you for three days, Guy."

Guy loved the attention and the compliments that Marianne lavished on him. He said, "I don't like being away from my family either, but I had to finish the recording in Haiti so that we can sell this record and I can take care of the trio of love."

He had originally referred to himself, Marianne and me as the 'trilogy of love.' But Mama Francine corrected him, saying, "A trilogy is an ensemble of three tragedies over a common theme, the child being adopted, the mother being dispossessed after giving birth, and the father finding out about it after three decades. But it should be simplified to a 'trio of love' because it's purer, and more musical; like a piano, violin, and cello, a beautiful trio, a joyous trio in love."

Guy added, "I want to take care of you, Marianne and that will require touring again to promote this newest release, but you and Robaire can tour with me."

Her eyes lit up like a Christmas tree. They both lit up cigarettes almost simultaneously, Marianne beating him to the draw by just a second. She had spent a long day on airplanes without the ability to smoke, and she was ready to have her moment of relaxation.

Guy said, "Do you remember when it was cool to smoke?" He added between puffs, "When we were young, you were nobody if you did not smoke, and now we are being ostracized for it."

She agreed. They shared two daily habits that were not only habitual but bonding as well. Smoking cigarettes and drinking coffee. And they absolutely loved to do both. It was possible to throw a third habit in too, but it was more of a treat than anything else. That was candy and chocolate. I wondered how they would ever fall asleep with all of the caffeine coursing through their veins, but they managed that just fine.

Marianne always looked forward to drinking coffee with Guy because the Haitian coffee was delicious and impossible to find in Seattle. They drank it out of the little tiny cups no bigger than a shot glass, because it was that strong.

Guy had a concert that evening at the Sheraton's grand ballroom, and Marianne was eager to attend considering it had been thirty two years since she last saw him perform live. When she got dressed for a nice evening, she was always stunning, and easily the most elegant woman in the room. Guy just loved the attention they got when they both dressed up for an evening out. His concerts were always Black- tie affairs, and he was elegance personified. The way that his crisp white shirt and black tie contrasted against his dark brown skin, coupled with his European etiquette and charm, gave him a certain charisma that was undeniable. He had Marianne seated at a table in the front at a forty- five-degree angle from his piano, where he could easily see her and sing to her. How his eyes lit up with excitement just as he hit a certain note. Marianne watched as he courted her with a song just as he had in that passionate summer of 1962. That was Vancouver, British Columbia, this was The Bahamas, but the electrical current that ran from his large round coffee-colored eyes to her electric blue eyes was extremely familiar. Guy's charisma was legendary, but it was brought back to life and heightened by his muse, his great love, his Anne-Marie duRosier. He had taken to calling her by his last name as if they were married and actually introducing her as his wife. Marianne obliged the ruse playfully and always blushed when he introduced her that way.

After Guy's show, he joined Marianne at her table and within moments the staff of the Sheraton's restaurant had wheeled out a beautiful dessert cart for them. They were both chocolate fiends and so devoured their mudslides together.

People occasionally passed by the table to congratulate the 'Maestro' on another captivating performance, and Guy would always stand and shake their hands then bow gracefully as they exited.

Marianne said with a hint of mischief, "Guy there is a casino in the hotel, and I think it would be fun to go play the slot machines, don't you?"

Guy was never one to gamble, but he obliged Marianne and they got up and made their way over to the dollar slot machines. Guy watched Marianne plop coin after coin into the slot machines.

"Darling, I am a conservative, a republican, who wears only Bostonian shoes, so you must forgive me for cringing while our money disappears into a machine."

She laughed heartily at Guy and kept slipping coins in until a bevy of buzzers and whistles went off and several hundred coins came pouring out into Marianne's machine, even spilling out onto her lap. Guy freaked out. Ever the musician, Guy likened the noise it made upon her winning to that of a concerto complete with gong, whistles, and triangle. He would have liked to conduct what he was hearing. Then he got scared.

"Marianne," he said firmly, "Collect that money and let's get out of here."

She again laughed at him with excitement until she saw that he was serious.

"This is Third World darling, and the dubious may be lurking, watching."

He was always careful, always on the precipice of paranoia, a trademark of the country of his birth.

They took the bounty home and Marianne divided up the winnings with Guy. Guy put the coins on his kitchen counter, which was a mess, and laid them out in a haphazard manner that would have had Mama Francine calling him 'Beethoven' again.

"Guy, I don't know how you ever find anything here."

Guy looked surprised, then defended himself and his mess saying, "There is order in my disorder."

He waited for his little play on words to sink in on Marianne and hoped to get a laugh out of her. Once he saw that she was about to smile, he broke into a riotous laugh that caused him to lie down and squirm on the bed, pounding one fist into the pillow and bellowing all the while.

When Marianne told me that they had a lot of fun together, she was not kidding around at all.

My birthday had arrived, and I was always happy for the day to come more so than any other holiday. I tried to do things every year to make it special. I remembered fondly that last year Marianne and I had gone to Jamaica together and had discovered, from Ethel St. Claire in the Miami airport, that Papa was alive. This year I wasn't doing anything significant and wished I was in the Bahamas with my mother and father. Just to say those words gave me an exhilarating feeling. *My mother and father.* It sounded so beautiful to me.

My birthday gift arrived in the mailbox in the now familiar brown envelopes stamped 'air mail' on them with eight to ten stamps from the Bahamas. First I opened an envelope that was addressed with Marianne's handwriting. Her lovely card read:

Happy Birthday to my sweet, handsome, son.

Today is my son's very special day. God was so good to give you back to me. I love you in every way. You're such a fine young man and I'm so proud that you're my son. June fifth was without a doubt the best day of my life. Thank you for wanting to find me. I hope you'll always love me just half as much as I love you!

Love,

Mom

I read it over and over again about five times because it was one of those beautiful moments in life that can't be glossed over quickly and put aside. I practically memorized it. I was never going to love my mother half as much as she loved me. No, I would always love her as much or more than she loved me. What she didn't realize yet was that I had always loved her with all of my heart even in the quietest solitude of my unknowing youth.

There was more inside of the envelope that I hadn't gotten to yet. I reached in and pulled out a piece of plain white paper with a few typewritten lines on it. It was my first telegram. It was from Guy and it read:

"On this commemorative day of your birth I am celebrating the nobleness of your heart and soul."

Love **Father**

There were the words, the sweetest words, from the sweetest pair that love had ever ordained. I reveled in the words and was comforted by them. Could Shakespeare have designed a sweeter, more compelling love story?

The next afternoon I got an alarming phone call from Marianne that just about gave me a heart attack.

She sounded very frightened, "Robert, I'm in the hospital with your father. He has had a severe seizure and he's in intensive care right now, but the doctor thinks he is going to stabilize as soon as he is able to get his high blood pressure under control."

I was shocked to hear the news but I played back the scene in my mind inside of his car when he had that involuntary jerking movement with his leg, and I opted not to say anything to him.

"Robert, your father has been going to a bush doctor for his high blood pressure rather than seeing a conventional physician. I met her yesterday. Her name is Billy; she's as tiny as a blade of grass, and she's an old Haitian woman. Her husband's name is 'Shoe', just like a tennis shoe. They are a cute little couple but I don't think the herbs and things were going to solve Guy's problems."

"He was seeing a bush doctor? You've got to be kidding me, Mom!"

Guy was as refined a man as there ever was, yet he still clung to certain Haitian customs at the expense of all conventional wisdom.

"Mom, I can't lose that man after only one year. I simply can't, because it would kill me." I started to break up a little bit on the phone, but Marianne reassured me that he was over the worst of things and that the doctor had prescribed some *dilantin* to offset the painful effects of his seizure. Marianne hung up quickly, saying she wanted to go back to emergency to be by his side.

I set the phone down, my head spinning with the introduction of fear and dread of losing the one person whom I had grown most completely attached to in my entire life. Guy had become my compass, my soul mate, and my friend, to the extent that we were so much alike we could read each other's minds and moods instantaneously. History books had indicated that the ancient aboriginal people of Australia could communicate nonverbally and always knew what was being thought before it was ever spoken. Guy and I shared this type of symbiotic relationship to a lesser extent.

As Guy began to recover, his first reaction to his doctor was, "I cannot stay here; I have to tour and sing with my son to promote the release of my latest recording."

The doctor thought Guy was delirious and smiled, pointing a finger at Marianne asking, "Who is this person?"

Guy answered promptly, "This person is called Marianne duRosier, my one and only wife that I love dearly."

Only then did the doctor realize that Guy was conscious. Guy had to confess, "It is unusual that a person just out of a seizure tells his doctor that he has to rush to sing, but this trio does things that are inaccessible to the common of mortals."

When the doctor left the room, Guy looked around and saw other patients on respirators that came down from the wall. He said to Marianne, "Get me out of here, darling, these people are breathing out of saxophones."

She laughed and laughed admitting that the respirator's shape did in fact take on the "J" shape of a saxophone. "Guy, you have a one-track mind for music."

"Marianne, get into bed with me."

She laughed nervously then chided Guy, "Not here. I can't get into bed with you in the hospital."

"Why not darling?" The nurses were all in love with Guy and his charm just like everyone who ever met him was, so Marianne thought they could have probably pulled it off but she was too nervous to climb into bed with him in the hospital.

The next day he was released into Marianne's custody, and he asked her to drive by the Buena Vista where he was hired as the musical director, so that he could chat with the owner about his eventual return to work. Stan, the owner, came to the top stair to greet them. He wagged a finger in jest at Marianne, "So you are trying to kill my maestro, Marianne?"

The other Haitians who worked there as waiters also began to congregate, and they all joked around with Guy, insinuating that his seizure was from too much sex.

Marianne and Guy caught on quickly to the jokes and Marianne blushed a deep red, shook her head back and forth, and smiled saying, "I didn't do it."

Marianne spent the entire drive to the airport thinking of ways in which she could move to Nassau to be with Guy permanently, but she knew that at the least she had the capacity to fly to her love as often as she wished.

Back inside the familiar Nassau airport, Marianne held onto Guy ever so tightly and they kissed and kissed in an attempt to prolong the inevitable departure. Neither of them cared who was watching because they were breathing life into one another and with each tender kiss, with each shared breath, their lives were changing for the better. Theirs was a love that so many would never know. A poetic love that did not choose its target based on income, or family arrangement, or anything other than love. They had willed into each other's lives poetry, adventure, and above all, love. Not an artful, posthumous love, but the love that overthrows life. They did not know if ruin or rapture awaited them, they only knew that with each embrace, with each kiss, there was a riot in their hearts.

Marianne had a way of looking inside of Guy and communicating tenderness so candid that he knew it was possible to withstand their cruel separation, while attempting to keep despair from invading his soul. Her searing blue eyes were the only light capable of illuminating the path of his solitude. Inside of their kiss, Guy could no longer ascertain where he ended and Marianne began, as she had become his essence and he, her light. She knew that the only remedy to cure this bittersweet, painful, tragedy was the permanent reunification of father, mother, and son.

"Guy," she said, as she picked up her suitcase in preparation for boarding, "There are only two things we can do. I must move here with you, or you must move to Seattle so that we can be together."

Guy answered obediently as he so often did, "Yes, darling."

Marianne's unabashed sorrow was felt by all those around her onboard the aircraft. Her eyes betrayed her at the most inconvenient times by completely giving her emotions away, and her sorrow was deep, the type that could only be accompanied by separation from the love of her life.

13

ALCHEMY

I T is remarkable what seventy-two minutes of John Coltrane unin-terrupted can do to one's psyche. Never before had I met someone who could sit in front of two great speakers and listen from start to fin-ish without speaking a word, to the greatest tenor saxophone player the world has ever known. Guy and I sat transfixed while 'Coltrane Plays the Blues' wafted throughout the walls of the house and our minds. It was a quartet, consisting of Coltrane himself, McCoy Tyner on the piano, Steve Davis on bass, and Elvin Jones on drums. Occasionally, I would look up at Guy and he was in a trance, living inside of the speaker somewhere, anticipating the next few bars along with the im-provisational genius at the sax. This is what religion was like without all of the posturing for money, power, and prestige. There is something in music that gives us an enduring sense of the human spirit that also gives us a sense of something outside of ourselves, and allows us an in-dividual version of the world that is so empowering.

My version of the world was changing monthly, daily, even by the hour with an arbitrary caprice. Lost inside of one of Coltrane's tracks, I reminisced about what had finally brought Guy back to Marianne and me on a full-time basis, in Seattle. Shortly after Marianne returned from her trip to Nassau, I phoned Guy while on one of my layovers in San Francisco, hoping to catch up with him and get his impression on his time together with Marianne. For the first few moments, every-thing was normal. We exchanged our usual greetings and genuine joy at the sound of each other's voices, but then everything changed in an instant. In the background I heard a blood chilling scream from whom I suspected to be Adriana, the young woman who sat at the cash register near the dining room of the prestigious Buena Vista Resort. A second later, Guy dropped the receiver hard to the floor then I heard some wrestling around and more screaming from Adriana. Just then, the phone went dead. I wondered what kind of insanity I just bore witness to, and I felt a sense of dread overcome me all at once. I tried in vain to call back several times, until about ten minutes later I got through. One ring, then two, three and four, I prayed for someone, anyone to answer that phone.

"Buena Vista," I heard Adriana say in an uncommonly frightened tone.

"Adriana, this is Robert, Guy's son. What is going on there?" I said with hesitation, almost not wanting to hear her answer.

"Oh Robert, I'm so sorry, we've just been robbed and your father was pistol whipped by three men wearing hoods. They thought he was on the phone with the police so they hit him over the head with a gun. He's on his way to the hospital right now."

I asked her for the number to the hospital and I dropped the phone. I couldn't believe that I had called at the exact moment of a robbery and that the call was the cause of Guy's beating at the hands of robbers. For the second time in two weeks, Guy was in the hospital, and I felt like I was being given a warning of some sort. I said the same sort of earnest prayer for his recovery as I did when I was a small child, sleeping in a dark, downstairs room asking for my real mother and father to be returned to me at any cost. I had made more than my share of promises with God in return for his favor of returning my mother and father to me, but I couldn't fathom having Guy given to me then taken so swiftly, almost in the same breath. I dealt not for that.

I called Marianne as quickly as I could and told her what had just happened while I was on the telephone, and she couldn't believe it either. We both agreed to call the hospital and whoever got through first would call the other back. After a few hours I was informed that Guy had been treated for a concussion and that I would be able to speak with him the following morning. When I got him on the telephone, I had only one thing on my mind.

"Papa, you are moving here with us. I won't have it any other way and I'm telling you right now that I'll get you a green card or whatever it takes for you to stay."

He had never heard me so dogmatic before and he agreed, "Robaire, can you imagine a balladeer being pistol whipped? It is completely incongruent." With his usual flair for words, Guy had done it again, describing his beating with magnificent language. He added, "I have been waiting for your invitation back to the Pacific, however, I didn't anticipate the catalyst that would take me there." This was his unique way of saying "Yes, I'd love to move to Seattle with you and Marianne permanently."

Before me now, across the room about ten feet was this man, this unique man, listening to the last track of Coltrane's masterpiece with me, and we were enjoying the moment of a soul's enchantment, far more than our physical embodiment could have ever enjoyed. In eighteen years of very formal Catholic education and doctrine I did not once ever come this close to God, nor to another soul. The disc finished and Guy looked up at me just as I did the same.

"Robaire, what we have just witnessed is inaccessible to the common of mortal."

It wasn't the first or last time that I'd hear him say that he and I agreed.

"Yes Papa, if there is one thing that you and I are not, it is common."

Having him back in Seattle was great. As we drove down Interstate 5 into Seattle he was amazed by the five lane freeway, packed with speeding vehicles that all seemed to be moving frenetically to arrive at some unknown destination. Our destination that day was a mixing studio in Seattle that I had arranged an appointment with to take the master of our recording and compress the music into a finished product. We also were going to speak with a graphic designer to get some conceptual ideas for the cover of the compact disc.

When we arrived at Martin Audio, we were ushered into an engineer's room and asked to sit down before a bevy of giant speakers that were unforgiving in their clarity. Whenever Guy was involved in musical interests, he walked with a necessary arrogance that instantaneously commanded the entire room's respect, and it was no different in America amongst young engineers or graphic artists who had never before heard of Guy duRosier. They tended to him like he was royalty.

The brainiest-looking engineer entered the room and said, "Mr. du-Rosier," acknowledging both of us, "please have a seat here directly in front of this speaker. I am going to compress the sound exactly as you want it before we print your CDs."

Guy sat in a black leather recliner and listened as if his life depended on the sound. He had never before recorded with twenty-seven separate tracks, so in effect, he had to monitor and evaluate twenty- seven different sounds in one little song. The engineer was busy taking any imperfections out of the music, and working with Guy to alter treble or bass where it was needed. It was impressive how he could bring the violins seemingly closer or fade the saxophone, even giving certain sounds echos if need be. Guy was like a surgeon in his ability to remove this, tie that together, essentially reshaping his masterpiece. He was doing what he loved most, which was conducting and arranging music, and it wasn't lost on me that he was as happy as I had ever seen him, in his element, to be sure. He had never had his hands on this kind of technology inside of a recording studio and he could barely wait to hear the final, mastered version on these phenomenal speakers. The sound system in the room very nearly duplicated a live performance: it was that good.

The engineer said, "This should be an excellent finished product, but if you hear anything you want changed, just stop me and we'll address it."

Guy nodded as he reclined in his chair, giving me a look that I had come to know well, a look that said, "This guy knows what he is doing."

He used to say to me at moments when he was impressed, "Robaire, this is a b-i-g country."

The violins sounded glorious, far better than Guy or I even expected as the first track began to unwind. The compression wiped out any and all background sounds, which Guy had grown accustomed to from LPs, but this was his first recording to compact disc. It blew his mind! His voice was crisp, the clarity nearly duplicating the original take in front of his microphone. It was all he could do to contain himself. He looked at me and whispered, "This is gold, Robaire."

To be able to discern so many instruments at once and all in balance was a treat for the senses. I heard the rain stick in one ear, and a triangle in another, then a harp, then castanets, and on and on. We had one disc pressed just for our own enjoyment, and when we got up to leave the room, Guy bowed gracefully in acknowledgement of the engineer's expertise. He said, "Merci beaucoup, monsieur."

The engineer had thoroughly enjoyed his time with us, saying, "I have never worked with such interesting music. I typically work with the grunge bands around Seattle like Nirvana, Queensryche, or Heart's Wilson sisters." Guy had no idea who these bands were, but I assured him that they were world famous.

Before leaving, we stopped by the graphic artist's office where we were greeted by Olivier Melnick, whom I suspected from the telephone conversation to be French. Indeed he was, and it was a special treat for Guy to be able to speak French with Olivier. Fate had again been kind enough to deliver a French designer for the cover of our compact disc. A million miles away from Haiti, in a city not known at all for its French contingent, here was our very own French graphic designer. It made sense. After all, peculiar things seemed to happen all the time around Guy, coincidences were no longer an explanation. It went beyond that into the realm of fate, where I was very comfortable.

I was out of the loop for about fifteen minutes while Guy took the opportunity to speak in his native tongue with Olivier Melnick. Olivier took a break for a moment to remark, "Your father speaks better French than I do, and I was raised in Paris. I've never heard a Haitian speak such eloquent French. How come you don't speak French?"

That was a question I had become accustomed to dodging because to address it would have taken telling our lives' story, and I was not about to divulge that to just anyone. I would just say, "Oh, I'm learning. Guy was always touring when I grew up." They'd usually leave it alone with that.

We were able to agree on a concept for the cover, and I made an appointment to return with some photographs and text the following week.

I had a big surprise in store for Guy on the drive home. He had dropped a few little hints to me here and there that he would like to obtain a visa to be able to stay in the United States indefinitely. I had started a record company called 'Thesaurus Records Inc.,' with the guidance of two entertainment attorneys, initially to protect Guy's interests in his licensing, and to possibly recover lost monies from his previous recordings and sales of his music. The lead attorney, Lance Rosen, suggested that I file what was called an O-1 visa on Guy's behalf. It was a special visa that was granted only to musicians of world-renown status.

It granted them permanent residency in the United States with the ability to earn money in the country. It was exactly what Guy needed, but Mr. Rosen suggested to me that he would have to prove soundly that Guy was indeed worthy of this visa. I grinned and lay on him a stack of documents and signatures from Ambassadors, mayors, dignitaries and the like, that would attest to his musical pedigree. Lance fashioned what was a very direct, well-written resume on Guy's behalf and sent it off to The American Federation of Musicians of the United States and Canada.

Office of the Secretary-Treasurer/United States Department of Justice
   Stephen R. Sprague
   American Federation of Musicians
   1501 Broadway, Suite 600
   New York, NY 10036-5503
   RE: O-1 visa request on behalf of Guy duRosier

Dear Mr. Sprague:
Mr. duRosier was born March 1, 1932. He is an internationally renowned composer, singer, pianist, organist, clarinetist, and saxophonist from Haiti. He was educated at Saint Louis de Gonzague, and has a degree in Humanities from Lycee Toussaint Louverture, in Haiti. He studied saxophone under the tutelage of famed jazz musician Billy Taylor in 1955 and later performed and recorded with Mr. Taylor. He also studied musical harmony and film scoring at the Berklee College of Music in Boston in 1972.

As a result of his worldwide travels and his commitment to his audiences, as well as his native intelligence, Mr. duRosier speaks and writes fluent French, English, Portuguese, and Creole. He is also a student of Latin.

His first musical composition, "Ma Brune," was an international best seller, topping musical charts throughout the Caribbean, Central and South America, France and the French speaking countries of the world. Since then, he has composed more than thirty original compositions, many of which are now classics in their genre.

Among his live concerts, perhaps his most notable was on May 4, 1969, at New York's Carnegie Hall. Mr. duRosier had a diplomatic passport enabling him to appear and perform in a solo concert at the famed venue. He was the second black performer to give a solo concert at Carnegie Hall, preceded only by Harry Belafonte.

Shortly after the Carnegie Hall concert, Mr. duRosier performed in concert in Paris where he was hailed by the media. He was described as "The Living Breath of Haiti," by the legendary Edith Piaf.

Other international concerts were performed in Bombay, Munich, Rio de Janeiro, Nassau, Tokyo— indeed, throughout the world. When Mr. duRosier appeared at the 1965 Miami International Festival of Music, he was the Honored Guest of the City of Miami.

Mr. Guy duRosier has been honored with numerous international acknowledgements in recognition of his extraordinary talent as a musician and composer. As recently as four months ago, Mr. duRosier received a Certificate of Recognition from the City of Boston, in recognition of his fifty years "of masterful musical compositions and unforgettable performances you have produced to sing the glories and beauties of Haiti, while enriching the life of all mankind."

Among his many other prestigious awards are his assignation as a Knight of the Grand Croix, bestowed in Geneva at the United Nations Palace, in 1972. He received the award at a ceremony in Haiti along with Edson Arantes do Nascimento (a.k.a. Pele) and Muhammad Ali.

Since 1986, Mr. duRosier has been performing regularly in the Bahamas and Haiti, primarily in two venues—at the Buena Vista Hotel in Nassau and at the United States Embassy to the Bahamas, at the invitation of the Honorable Carol Hallet, United States Ambassador to the Bahamas. His audiences at the embassy have included international heads of state, military leaders, and dignitaries such as Sidney Poitier and Richard Widmark.

Over his enduring career, Mr. duRosier has released literally dozens of albums on many record labels, including La Belle Creole Records, Gaydem Records, and Decca Records. His most recent release, 'Reminiscences Haitiennes,' was recorded in Haiti with a selection of musicians from the Haitian Philharmonic, St. Trinite.

Thank you for your consideration.
Lance S. Rosen
Koler, Rosen, and Fitsimmons

I assumed that obtaining Guy's visa, if possible, could take up to a year. So it was with great elation that I had fielded a jubilant call from Lance Rosen the following week. "Robert, would you believe after just six weeks, your approval for an O-1 visa for your father has come? I'm looking at it right now."

I was so happy for Guy and now we were on our way up to Lance's office, to Guy's surprise, to collect his visa.

We were met at the front office as usual by Lance, and he had on one hand a handshake for Guy, and in the other, a sealed envelope. We thanked him and sat down to open it. Guy read it first and showed only a tempered enthusiasm as he asked me to read it to him aloud.

Office of the Secretary Treasurer
Stephen R. Sprague
1501 Broadway, Suite 600
New York, NY
10036-5503
January 10, 1997
Lance S. Rosen
Koler, Rosen, and Fitsimmons
615 Second Ave.
Seattle, Wa. 98104
RE:O-1 Visa consultation on behalf of Guy duRosier

Dear Mr. Rosen:
We have reviewed the Draft I-129 Petition and supporting documents regarding your request for our advisory opinion on behalf of the above-referenced Haitian artist.

Based upon the new applicable statutory and regulatory requirements, it is our advisory opinion that the evidence presented clearly established that Guy duRosier is a recording artist of extraordinary ability, which has been demonstrated by sustained international acclaim. This artist does meet the recently revised standards of distinction in the arts to qualify for an O-1 visa.

Accordingly, we have no objection to the granting of this petition.
Very Truly Yours – Stephen R. Sprague.
Secretary-TreasurerAMF

When I finished reading the letter, Guy slapped me on the leg, "Robaire, you've done it!"

He jumped up to shake Lance Rosen's hand vigorously. Lance was as pleased for Guy as if he were family. He knew how especially difficult it was for Haitians to be granted visas in the United States. They were consistently being turned away and then held in detention at Guantanamo Bay. But Guy now had the ability to live the rest of his days in the United States if he so chose.

In the plush elevator, I pushed the button and it took a quick moment to reach the lobby, leaving Guy a brief opportunity to express his sentiments.

"Robaire, this is a country that is straight. Nothing oblique where law and order are concerned. Everything is straight man. Whatever it cost for this attorney, it is well worth it."

He held onto the approval paperwork gingerly, burning the words, *This artist does meet the standards for an O-1 visa*, into his mind. He held it against his chest and looked upward stating, "God is good."

When Guy shared the news with Marianne, she was delighted at the sudden real prospect that her love could stay with her in Seattle permanently. After she hugged Guy and me, Marianne proposed that we go out for a nice dinner, just the three of us.

Then she added to the euphoria with more great news, "While you were gone, someone from New York called to ask you to perform for a group called 'NOAH', which they said was the National Organization for the Advancement of Haitians." Then her eyes lit up and she said, "The concert will be held at the Waldorf Astoria Hotel in Manhattan, and they want to honor you with a living legend award."

By this time Guy was walking on air, his Bostonians never touching the ground. He sauntered over to Marianne and gave her a hug, saying "It is good to be wanted, darling."

She kissed him tenderly and then reminded him to return a call to the chairman of NOAH, Joseph Baptiste, so that he could arrange his travel accommodations.

While Guy spoke to Mr. Baptiste, Marianne and I sat on the sofa looking at his visa authorization in disbelief.

"Mom, I thought he would get it but it came so quickly, isn't that amazing?"

"It sure is."

We both watched as Guy became animated on the phone, showing off his youthful exuberance. He had a lot to be happy for this day.

When he got off of the phone, he translated the conversation for us and stated emphatically, "My darling, and my son, pack your bags for New York, we are going to Manhattan in two weeks." He did a little dance for us then sat beside Marianne and buried his face in the nape of her neck. When he came up for air he said, "I tell you."

That was all he said. We were left to fill in the blanks, but he said that a lot and we both knew what it meant. When a man who commands words the way he does finds himself at a loss for words, it can only be a very pure feeling. We both knew he was overwhelmed.

"Robaire," he added, "You will take the stage with me and we'll lay 'Do-do, Ti-ti' on them."

My mouth fell open and he had gotten his desired effect: surprise... no shock.

He added, "The award will be presented to me by the President of Haiti, Rene Preval, and the Chairman of the Black Congressional Caucus, Congressman Charles Rangel. The Prime Minister of Jamaica will also be there, and a young band called the 'Fugees.'"

I knew who the Fugees were, with Lauren Hill, Pras, and Wyclef Jean, and I had seen Congressman Rangel on CNN often, but to perform on stage in front of all of these people was going to be really fun.

14

THE STAGE

IT was a short walk from our table to the side of the stage where Guy and I waited patiently for the Fugees to finish accepting their award for Best Contemporary Haitian musicians of the year. We were surrounded by some of the most powerful, influential black men in the world. Guy had already mingled with them in the pre-ceremony VIP reception, so he stood patiently with his arms folded while going over his chords in his mind. Then, Charles B. Wrangle, United States Congressman and leader of the black congressional caucus, approached me, putting out his hand. The audience roared their appreciation for the Fugees as they concluded their acceptance speech, signaling our cue to take the stage. I shook Congressman Wrangle's hand and introduced myself to him.

"Good luck, son. You should be very proud of your father."

"Oh, I am sir. It is an honor to meet you," I answered, as I made my way up the series of steps leading to the large stage.

Guy was greeted with resounding applause as he accepted the Living Legend Award in appreciation for dedication to preserving the Haitian culture through music and entertainment. He made his way to the piano as I strode toward the center of the stage and grabbed the microphone, remembering to keep it about four inches from my mouth as Guy had repeatedly taught me.

I was suddenly grateful for my job as a flight attendant, not because I was afraid to perform, but because it put me in front of hundreds of people continually, and for that reason, I was not nervous at all, even on the stage of one of the grandest hotels in the world, the Waldorf Astoria.

Marianne had suggested that I think of Mama Francine while I sang 'Do-do, Ti-ti' with Guy, so I looked out into the crowd of people, able only to distinguish faces that were silhouetted against the dimmed theater lights. Each face became my lovely grandmother and comforted me as I sang from my heart, together with my father on stage for the first time ever, knowing fully that the odds of this ever happening were staggering. I was floating and experiencing the euphoria that inevitably comes with tapping into your heart and soul and expressing yourself without reservation. There was nothing that could compare to this. We finished the song and I bowed, not knowing what to expect, when suddenly the room erupted in applause. Guy had chosen my indoctrination to the stage and to a glimpse of his lifestyle not at some small club or dinner theater but at the Waldorf Astoria Hotel in front of live television cameras and political and entertainment celebrities. I had passed my test. I walked over to the piano where he was waiting for me and we hugged each other as we exited the stage together. Waiting for us at the bottom of the stairs was David Dinkins, the ex-mayor of New York City, with a large grin on his face.

"Maestro duRosier," he said, "That was magnificent to see father and son perform together."

"Your excellency, allow me to introduce my son, Robaire duRosier."

I shook his hand and thanked him for his kind critique. We were surrounded by dignitaries, and Guy was right at home in their midst. If he weren't a musician, there is no question but that he would have made a fine president or senator.

"Robaire," Guy had always said, "Music is a true expression, while politics involves the cult of personality, and that can never be fully true. I prefer the virtue of music over the intoxication of personality."

I felt that virtue on the stage if only for five minutes; however, I also tasted a dose of intoxication at the pure euphoria that coursed through my veins while listening to a room explode with applause.

Marianne and Guy stood hugging each other and kissing in the hallway just outside our hotel room. I decided to patiently wait out their passion, considering it to be horrible etiquette to interrupt passion, even if I was dying to get out of my tuxedo and kick back. I was only on stage for five minutes but I was completely drained from the emotion and anxiety that accompanied the performance. Guy saw how tired I was and asked, "Robaire, will you be able to stay awake to meet your sister D'Jenane?" I had forgotten that she was going to come by the hotel that evening to meet Marianne and me.

"Oh yeah Papa, I'll be fine. I'm just relaxing."

Inside of the room Guy marveled at my flat feet and laughed as he took off his socks to see who had the flattest.

"Let your mother be the judge Robaire," he laughed as he placed his foot beside mine.

"Flat is flat," Marianne suggested as she couldn't decide whose feet were flatter. We were all laughing, but I was reminded of my youth and the countless trips to the podiatrist to figure out what was wrong with my feet, then the orthotics that were designed especially to go in all of my shoes so I could continue to compete in sports.

There was a knock at the door, and Guy sprung up out of his chair to fling the door open. Standing inside the open doorway was my sister D'Jenane.

With a very high-pitched voice, she said, "Hello Papa." Guy and D'Jenane hugged, then began speaking French with one another, then they would switch back and forth between English and French. D'Jenane was born and raised in Ecuador and Columbia while Guy was contracted to do film scoring and had his own variety show, so when she spoke English it was with the rapid fire countenance of the Spanish language.

"Hello my brother. How are you? I can't believe I have another brother. Where have you been?" It was like machine gun fire. Rat-a-tat-tat. Guy quickly chided her for too many questions and she obeyed, settling into a chair and exchanging greetings with Marianne. It was uncanny how Guy and I were alike to the bone. I didn't like personal questions much either. We both had this way of being vague, offering up only as much information as we were comfortable giving at any given time. We gave each other a look that went beyond understanding and grinned at each other. Marianne noticed and smiled along with us. She knew her two Pisces men better than most anybody.

The next morning Guy had a radio interview to do before we headed to LaGuardia for our return trip to Seattle. I was becoming adept at interpreting his French even if I only got bits and pieces of sentences. I knew he had made reference to his family, especially his lovely wife, Anne-Marie duRosier. He was beaming with pride over both his performance and his family. Marianne had transformed him back to his charming, handsome self, leaving no trace of the man I had met at the Nassau airport who was in his own words, "just waiting to die." I knew that I had rejuvenated him, but there was nothing like a good woman's love and affection to give a man back his youthful exuberance. The nice thing about it was that Marianne was served as well. She looked like a glamorous queen, even regal standing beside her man.

I hugged D'Jenane goodbye and promised to stay in touch with her when I got back home. She was a sweet girl and I knew that we had some connection that transcended the awkwardness of being half brother and sister, so I meant it when I told her not to worry, that we would see each other again soon.

I sat across the aisle from Guy and Marianne and when I turned to say something to them, I noticed that they were fast asleep, her head tucked into his shoulder and his laid back against the seat back. I took advantage of a moment to think about what it was that had me so incredibly connected to my father. Then I realized that he was not only my compass in life but he was, more importantly, the antidote to all of my insecurities. He was an intellectual, accomplished, achievement-oriented man, and in him all of the racial inequities I had suffered were laid bare and forever gone. I didn't realize how badly I needed that for my self-esteem, and to clear the path ahead of me that was full of opportunities that I hadn't pursued.

We weren't home long when Guy came practically skipping into the front room to tell me we were going to Newark to do a show at the Center for the Performing Arts theater in two weeks, and that directly after that show, we were booked at the prestigious Lincoln Center in Manhattan. It was quite an adrenaline rush for both of us, and I recognized that a musician is only as good as his last performance. Who ever knew when the next one was coming or if it would ever come? But I never worried about that with Guy because he had such an incredibly loyal, patriotic following all over the Eastern seaboard and the Caribbean.

"Robaire," Guy remarked, "when you take the stage with me in New Jersey, I want you to take a few moments and speak with the crowd so that they can get to know you. It will be your proper introduction to the Haitian community. And I want you to do a solo that we are going to have to practice every day so that you can get the Creole accent just right. The song is called 'Yo-yo' and it is a beloved folkloric merengue piece that I will arrange for you. I'd like to get into the studio and record it sometime this week so that we can send it to the Haitian radio stations in Jersey, then your audience will be hungry to hear the song live." For the next week I belted the new song out in the shower, on the airplane, in my car, in the gym, and just about everywhere I went. I had the Creole lyrics down to memorization and Guy comforted me by telling me that a slight accent would be charming to the Haitian audience. We booked a few hours in a studio in Seattle then went in and ripped the song in one single take. It came out perfectly! And Guy's arrangement was more lively and rhythmic than anything he had done in years as it contained marimbas, Brazilian percussion, and a driving baseline that gave the piece a relentless merengue flavor. Guy instructed me to sing the first verse in Creole, the second in French, and the last verse in English.

"The Haitians will recognize that the son is a polyglot just like his papa," Guy beamed with pride.

"Yeah papa, but I just hope they don't start talking to me in Creole or French after the show because they'll lose me after a few words," I laughed.

"Just nod your head Robaire and act aloof. An artist can get away with that, you know. Eccentricity is practically expected from an artist," Guy reasoned.

Guy and I laughed so hard when I told him that I would say "Merci," then duck out of the room like I had somewhere very important to go.

We made two or three copies of the single, then sent them off to Guy's contacts at radio stations in Haiti, New York, New Jersey, and Miami, in hopes of the song getting some airtime.

"Robaire, Haitians are going to be hearing you all over the East Coast and in Haiti in about a week," Guy said as he gauged how surprised I would be.

"No way, Papa," was all I could say. He gave me his look that said a thousand words. It could have been patented and sold to parents who were trying to shut their kids up without speaking. It was a look that said *don't you dare underestimate what a duRosier can do,* while simultaneously assuring me that he was telling me the truth. I, like no one else, could see through Guy's veiled layers of the truth because I was just like him. He was such a walking oxymoron because one moment he could be confused, helpless, haphazard, and completely disorganized, and the next he could be standing next to the President of Haiti, or a United States Congressman talking about politics. I was learning to trust what Guy was capable of and for just a half of a second wondered what it would be like to have a hit song and tour around the country with my father on a regular basis.

"duRosier," Guy commanded of Marianne in his new comical way of addressing her simply by his last name, "Would you mind if Robaire and I went golfing today?"

Marianne smiled back at him, adoring her new nickname and asked, "Do you feel like golfing today?"

"Kind of," Guy answered back shyly.

He was picking up American slang from me and it sounded so funny when he used it because we all knew he was dying to spend a few hours golfing, his true passion outside of music. He was downplaying his desire to go golfing by nonchalantly saying 'kind of,' but when Marianne told us to go have fun and that she'd have dinner waiting for us, he practically jumped off of the sofa to hug her and grab his clubs.

I didn't particularly like golf because I could never keep the ball on the course. I could crush it a mile but I never knew quite what direction the ball was headed after it left my club. I did, however, love the time outside with Guy and the chance to talk to him while getting some fresh air and some exercise, albeit for me it was an exercise in patience.

After we hit our tee shots from the first hole, we walked in unison to hit our second shot from the fairway, when Guy instructed, "Robaire, the quality that separates a professional singer from a journeyman is intonation. You must be able to evoke emotion from your crowd and the only way to do this is to leave your very soul on the stage. You must use your voice to command and to caress and this is accomplished by intonation. I learned this from Mama Francine, and in the end it is what separates me from all of the other Haitian balladeers. You must take the very note into the palm of your hand and caress it with tenderness to the point of whispering sometimes, then be able in one note's notice to command the room's attention with a thunderous delivery that lets them really feel the sound. I promise you that if you feel it on stage, then they will too."

Guy was on the green in three shots while I was praying I hadn't killed someone on the opposite fairway with a vicious three-wood hook. I hollered at Guy, "I'll be with you in a minute, Tiger."

Guy idolized Tiger Woods and even wore his trademark red shirt with black slacks. He raised his putter at me in acknowledgement and smiled broadly. After our round was finished, Guy complained to me of a strong headache and worried about his high blood pressure, but in the same breath dismissed it like it was just nothing. Marianne had taken Guy to see her family doctor, Dr. Tim Anderson, and he had Guy's blood pressure problem under control, but I knew he should get back in to see him if possible before our trip to New York.

We came home to a fantastic dinner being prepared by Marianne. The wonderful scent of spices in the house was comforting and I watched as Guy danced around the corner and into the kitchen to hug his darling little girl, his Anne-Marie. As I watched their mutual affection, I understood that people need lovers because it makes the everyday things seem magical. Suddenly, preparing a meal becomes a sensuous event as this thing called love colors everything in its path with a more vibrant shade of its original color. It always had a tremendous effect on my metabolism to see my mother and father in love. It helped me to better understand the journey that my life was, and if real love was the payday for some suffering, then the reward was worthwhile and the journey not in vain.

"Mom, that meal was $29. 95 a plate," I smiled. I had started to rate Marianne's meals with a price tag because it was my way of telling her how much I appreciated her food. She could have had her own restaurant indeed, the food was that good. In reality it was worth much, much more because her meals were prepared with an abundance of love that had no price tag, and she was sending off her two men, the loves of her life, to New York with nothing but sweet love.

The Newark airport was relatively easy to navigate as Guy and I found our way from our gate to the baggage claim area. As usual, Guy walked with his 'axe' in his left hand, never even considering for a moment checking his saxophone in with baggage claim. That was his baby, and his demeanor changed when he was toting it around with him as evidenced by his arrogant walk through the Newark airport. We arrived at baggage claim and were promptly met by three men who surrounded Guy with handshakes and wide smiles that illustrated the reverence they held for Guy. One of the men was a reporter, and the other two worked in promotion for the local radio station that was sponsoring the concert at the newly renovated Center for the Performing Arts Theater. One of the men quickly pulled a newspaper clipping from his briefcase to show Guy, and when I saw the advertisement for our concert over Guy's left shoulder I couldn't help but notice right next to my father's half page advertisement was a lovely picture of supermodel Cindy Crawford. He didn't even know who she was so I didn't bother telling him how proud he should be to share the page with her. Whenever there was the slightest hint of jealousy from Marianne, Guy would quell it by saying "duRosier, what is a sixty five years old man going to do except eat and sleep?"

Waiting outside for our transportation was a nice Lincoln Towncar that was driven by the reporter. They took us directly to the theater so that we could see the marquee and delight in the fact that Guy was sharing the marquee with Diana Ross. Her show would precede ours by one evening but it was thrilling to see his name in lights with an American diva of her stature. None of these things affected Guy, but I was thrilled by it all because it was all so new to me. We were dropped off at the Hilton beside Penn Station that afternoon and we took advantage of the evening to rest from our long flight and have room service.

"Tomorrow we have to take the subway into New York for rehearsal in mid town, Robaire," Guy said.

I was thrilled because my last trip to New York was great, but we stayed at the Waldorf Astoria and didn't explore the city at all, and in my opinion you haven't really been in New York until you ride the trains and walk in the city. I was, however a bit worried when considering whether or not Guy could navigate his way around the city, because I knew that I certainly couldn't. The next morning would prove my worries useless.

As disorganized as Guy could be, he took New York by the reins like he owned the city, and I followed him onto the subway train in complete shock. I never saw him with this confidence outside of Haiti before, but he saw the shock on my face and reminded me, "Robaire, I lived and performed in New York. I jammed with Miles Davis several times, just follow me and look straight ahead when we get off of the train because New Yorkers can spot a tourist a mile away and we don't need to get mugged." I liked the new assertive nature I saw in my father, and I knew it was because he was in 'the city' of all cities, a place where musicians went to make or break their careers, and this was the place, after all, where Guy played Carnegie Hall nearly three decades prior.

We got off near Madison Square Garden and started walking with a speed and purpose that I quickly saw was a trademark of New York. Seattle, even after two or three lattes, was slower by far than this city. We had about eighteen blocks to cover in forty-five minutes in order to get to the rehearsal hall. That walk would come to define my vision of New York, and I was so grateful that Guy made me walk instead of grabbing a cab because what we saw was the essence of New York. We may as well have been in ten different countries in thirty minutes as we walked by a block that was completely Puerto Rican in every way, then a Cuban neighborhood on the next block, followed by a Middle Eastern section. Each block cordoned off the previous culture and it stopped immediately only to be replaced by a different one. There was no eye contact or 'hi, how's it going' to be shared here. No, this was a city of individuals that had been hardened by its very grandeur.

"Keep walking and do not look up at the skyscrapers Robaire," Guy demanded.

He didn't want me to be a target for a mugger, but it was almost impossible not to look up at the asphalt jungle. It was block after block of monstrously high buildings that left very little sky uncovered, until at last we came to the rehearsal hall and walked up the stairs to enter. Right away we were greeted by a handful of musicians, all whom rushed over to shake hands and exchange greetings with the 'Maestro.'

The acoustics in the room were enhanced by the hardwood floor, and in the center of the large hall sat a beautiful black baby grand piano that Guy was looking at out of the corner of his eye while talking with his band members. Soon enough he was seated at the piano warming up by going through some chords when he started to play a song that I didn't recognize, but as I observed all of the people in the room, they stood at attention and began singing along with Guy. It sounded very patriotic and when he was finished, Guy told me that he always liked to start his rehearsals off by playing the Haitian national anthem. I was surrounded by two generations of the best musicians Haiti had to offer. Sitting across from the piano on a bar stool with guitar in hand was Beethova Obas, perhaps Haiti's best young musician, and to his right was the beautiful young chanteuse, Emiline Michel. Next to Guy at the piano sat a wonderful piano player and Guy's contemporary, Ednar Guinard. Ednar was classically trained and Guy was self-taught, playing more of a melodic, rhythmic style that was less constrained than Ednar's style. They were peers but it didn't take long before they were arguing over who the finest jazz pianist was. Ednar mentioned somebody that Guy scoffed at and shot back, "Cyrus Chestnutt is the best piano player in the world." I felt proud because I had turned Guy on to Cyrus Chestnutt months ago and Guy marveled at his ability and now he was showing off his newfound knowledge of American jazz to his friends. Ednar didn't know who Chestnutt was so Guy, in his occasional snobby way, put his nose up in the air and said, "Then it is pointless to continue the argument if you don't even know who the best contemporary American jazz pianist is." I thought this was arguing but it was just typical Haitian bantering back and forth. Then they switched to speaking Creole and started laughing at each other.

I didn't need to rehearse because Guy and I had been over our song a million times, so I just sat back and listened to the rest of them working out the kinks between each other. Judging from the coordination between these great musicians, the show promised to be noteworthy, in part because Guy knew as an arranger that the success or failure of a show was determined by the preparation that went into the writing and rehearsal of the material.

After about two hours, we wrapped up the rehearsal and took a cab to Times Square where we looked for a restaurant. This place was like the center of a bee's nest, buzzing with activity and illuminated with bright neon lights everywhere you looked. This was it. We were in the epicenter of the greatest city in the world. Guy and I ducked into a restaurant and took off our coats as we were welcomed by a hostess and led to a table beside the window. Beside us sat a young family, the father roughly my age, and the children about two and four. This scene caused a stir in me that I never could have expected, as for a moment, I understood what I was missing out on in life. I wanted to be a father, and this was the first moment that I ever thought of it. I finally knew Guy so I felt free to be a father myself. How can a man be a father unless he has a father?

It was fortunate that Guy and I didn't have to chatter back and forth all of the time because I was lost in a daydream, inside of a kaleidoscope of thoughts, hopes, and dreams, and Guy left me to my moments of silence. In my mind, I imagined a mobile hanging above my head spinning around slowly. This mobile had six separate wire arms that held wire-shaped teardrops, and inside of each teardrop was a round mirror that showed me six separate images of my life. In one, I was standing with my hands in my pockets in Ivo Bannister's garage, frightened but determined to find out who my real mother and father were. In another, I saw Marianne standing in a white sundress in the Seattle airport, with the beginning of a smile coming to the corner of her mouth. In a third, I held Molly's hand tightly as she walked a scared ten year old up the front stairs of my childhood house and explained to me why I wasn't yet adopted. In still another, I saw Ethel St. Claire recognize me as a Haitian and revealing to me that I had a father whom she would attempt to find for me. I saw Christmas mornings and trees filled with tinsel and ornaments, with presents underneath the tree, but without the two things that I wished for every year, and never got from Santa Claus, my mother and father. And in the sixth round mirror, I saw a beautiful vision of myself with a child, a little girl who was all mine, and the joy on her face filled me with a peace that was otherwise unknowable. She had the confident look of a child who knew who she was and where she had come from. I saw her skipping down a hallway to her bedroom where she waited for me to read her a bedtime story, then we said a prayer together and kissed goodnight. I couldn't ever remember skipping as a child and this was a vision of pure happiness. I knew that a child had to be happy in order to skip. Then this wondrous mobile disappeared and left me with the wonderful discovery that I would someday become a father, and if there were one thing that I would ever do in this life of mine, I would be a good father to a child and ensure that this child would grow up without fear as a constant companion. This child would skip, and my soul would be enriched because of it.

Guy's face slowly came into focus and he simply stared at me and nodded his head as if to say, "Welcome back, Robaire." He didn't ask me what I was daydreaming about. That just wasn't our way. We didn't dig into each other's thoughts that way, we simply were all about loving each other today, and for the rest of the tomorrows that we had together.

The next evening, we were picked up and driven to the Center for the Performing Arts Theater in New Jersey where we again saw Guy's name in bright lights on the marquee next to Diana Ross's name. I thought about snapping a photograph of it but took a picture with my mind instead, not wanting to cheapen the moment any. We were escorted back- stage where several of the musicians were already gathered. It was very interesting to watch each performer's pre-show behavior because some were very nervous, some drank to calm their nerves, and then there was my father who barely had a heartbeat, he was so calm. He had been doing this since the age of fourteen and a stage was like home to him so he relaxed on a sofa and fielded questions from two newspaper reporters and two radio personalities. Oddly, I was not the least bit nervous either, given the enormity of the evening. The crowd was expected to be in the thousands, and this was a real theater as opposed to the banquet room setting at the Waldorf Astoria the previous month. Guy's demeanor calmed me but the same couldn't be said for the pianist Ednar Guinard as I witnessed him drink a six-pack of beer in about ten minutes. He was loosening up with each empty can.

When Guy finished his interviews, he sat and told jokes in Creole with some of the band members and he once again had the whole room laughing. Then the program director came into the room and signaled that it was time for the young sensation, Beethova Obas to take the stage.

"Emiline, you will follow Beethova on my cue, then Maestro duRosier and Robaire will take the stage," he said as he adjusted his headset to hear more clearly what his assistants were saying.

It was not what one would expect from a rock concert, but there was definitely the same element of attention on a smaller scale as people darted in and out of Guy's dressing room, one to check if we needed something to drink, another to offer makeup, and several people wanting to shake Guy's hand and introduce themselves. Ednar's condition was worsening, prompting Guy to give me 'the look.' His furrowed brow was a certain signal of disapproval, and I had seen this look last at the Duvalier airport in Haiti when Guy had to intercede on my behalf and shoo away the mob of Haitian beggars. He said to me in almost a whisper, "Robaire, just remember you are a duRosier and everything will be fine." I nodded, "Right on, Papa," and Guy smiled. He loved my American slang and used it every chance he got. He especially liked 'right on'. I added another level of slang when I said, "We're gonna flip 'em out papa." The crowd roared and we were brought back into focus as Beethova Obas finished his set. I was alarmed at the amount of noise the applause generated and thought to myself, '*wow, there are a lot of people out there.*'

The busy program director located the elegant young Emiline Michel in the hallway and hurriedly motioned her to take the stage as Beethova Obas came off exuberantly, with sweat on his brow and a big smile on his face. Emiline Michel was radiant in a shimmering gold gown, but it was difficult to tell which was brighter, her smile or her dress. Guy wanted to be one of the first to congratulate Beethova on his performance, ever mindful of his graciousness and etiquette. Beethova peeked his head inside of our dressing room and said to me in French, "Good luck, petite duRosier." The performers had taken to calling me "little Guy" because of my resemblance to Guy. "Merci beaucoup, Monsieur Obas," I answered. With just fifteen minutes or so left before I was going to go on stage with Guy, he came back into the room and suggested we make some changes to the song, 'Do-do, Ti-ti.'

"Robaire," Guy questioned, "I think we should sing the song backwards so to speak. What I mean is, let's open with the bridge, the part of the song you wrote, sleep, sleep, sleep, and may your dreams be realized, then move into the chorus afterwards."

Ever complaisant, I agreed to the changes heartily.

"I will play an introductory interlude on the piano, then I'll nod my head to you when it is time for you to come in," he directed. For a moment, I thought I could use a six-pack of beer myself, but I soon calmed my nerves and was anxious as could be to get onto that stage with my father.

We were on! Guy quickly said to me, "Let me take the stage first and greet my people, then I will introduce you. When you hear your name, I want you to join me on stage and 'flip them.'"

I chuckled at Guy's attempt to use the slang I was teaching him, then recomposed myself and shook his hand. He bounced gracefully up the steps that led to the giant stage, then bowed twice before taking his seat at the beautiful, black grand piano. He adjusted the microphone, pulling it closer to his mouth and engaged the crowd in French. For a moment, I felt just like I was back in the on-deck circle waiting to stride to the plate with my bat on my shoulder, facing a tough pitcher with the game on the line. It was a nervous feeling, but it was a 'good nervous' energy that reminded me I was really a-l-i-v-e and ready to assert myself in a positive way. It was a complete galvanization of my entire physiology.

Guy spoke my name and that was my cue. Up I stepped, feeling so very light on my feet, until I breezed by Guy and strode confidently toward the microphone at the center of the stage. The lights were bright and shining directly in my face, and as I scanned the audience, all I could see were the silhouettes of thousands of faces.

The butterflies were gone. I was right at home, just like my father, the maestro.

"Good evening ladies and gentleman," I announced. "On behalf of my father, Guy duRosier, please allow me to introduce myself. My name is Robert duRosier and I'd like to say that it is an honor and a pleasure to be here in New Jersey, on this grand stage together with my father. We'd like to dedicate this opening piece to the children of Haiti, and to all Haitian parents who have undoubtedly sung this beautiful, delicate, lullaby, 'Do-do, Ti-ti,' to their children."

I could hear the audience gasp in recognition of this classic lullaby and after a few seconds, Guy started in on a magnificent piano solo that smoothly wound its improvisation around the chords of the song until at last, the melody became recognizable to myself and to the audience. There was genius in his composition because you could recognize the melody but never ascertain which direction he was headed next. It was as if Schubert were playing his own classical version of Rock-a-bye-baby in an American comparison. The Haitians were on the edges of their seats and I could hear whispers of wonder, of awe. Then, Guy nodded distinctly in my direction and I began.

"Sleep, sleep, sleep, and may your dreams be realized." I was the perfect person at the perfect moment to sing such a message to children, and to the child in all of us grown or not. My sleep was uneasy, but I managed to dream every single night of a better reality, and I was living, breathing proof on this stage that your dreams can come true. I moved into the chorus and began to sing the Creole that the Haitians were familiar with, "Ma le la rie veeay, la rie veeay sae shae, Ma lay luh luh mae, luh luh mae sae shae. Mrah contray yu blah, oh lan dae, kee top kupay bwah; blah kupay bwah, bwah kupay blah."

Guy then joined me in the second verse, and it was then that I began to hear the Haitian women sniffling and sobbing in the first few rows. I removed the microphone from its stand and walked to the edge of the stage where I got down on one knee and rocked back and forth to Guy's wonderful melody, simulating a baby being rocked back and forth by the rhythm of the song. We harmonized the ending, "Sil li pas do do, crab la va mange, sil li pas do do, crab la va mange."

The Haitian women were now almost all weeping as they had likely never seen father and son, two generations, singing such a delicate song that was a part of the fabric of their lives. I stood up straight when the song ended and I wondered what to expect, when suddenly a booming, thunderous applause reached out from the theater and swallowed us up whole. They were all on their feet and the lights panned the audience so that I could finally see them. What I saw, I will never forget. Everyone was on their feet, everyone. Men and women were clapping with handkerchiefs in their hands, leaning against each other for support. I looked at Guy, and he was beaming. He made a gesture toward me as if to say, "Bow, Robaire, bow." I did so and the audience clapped even louder. Within the applause, I heard shouts of "Vive Haiti, vive Haiti," and "Bravo duRosier," "Encore duRosier," and I was frozen on that stage, content to spend the whole evening with these people. Finally, I put the microphone back in its stand at the center of the stage, bowed once more, and walked over to where Guy was still seated at the piano. He stood up to hug me, kissed me on the forehead, and we turned and bowed once more together and the room exploded again. Guy whispered in my ear, "You killed them, my son." Later, he would tease me mercilessly about not leaving the stage. I did not want to, and he was right. It was like no other feeling in the world.

I would share the stage several more times with Guy, but nothing ever compared to the pure euphoria that I experienced at the Center for the Performing Arts Theater that evening.

The one who bows and pays respect,
And the one who receives the bow and respect,
Both of us are empty.
That is why the communion is perfect.
Thich Nhat Hanh – "The Heart of Understanding"

Part V

THE QUICKENING

*"Let me not pray to be sheltered from dangers but to be fearless in facing them.
Let me not beg for the stilling of my pain but for the heart to conquer it."*
SIR RABINDRANATH TAGORE

15

THE PACIFIC

"Black and white is outta sight," I shouted at Guy and Marianne as they sat comfortably together on the sofa, daydreaming about their upcoming cruise to the Mexican Riviera. Marianne had the brochure open to show Guy the ship and all of the different ports of call that they would be visiting. I couldn't help but sing the famous Smokey Robinson song to them, "We're gonna fly away, glad you're goin' my way, I love it when we're cruisin' together." They both laughed hard at my little side-show and Guy said to Marianne, "Look what we made, darling!" Then he continued to tease me about not wanting to leave the stage in New Jersey saying, "Our son got himself a taste of show business and he is infected. Look, he still thinks he is on stage."

Marianne was pointing out all of the various stops on their cruise to Guy as he shifted closer to her on the sofa and adjusted his bifocals over the bridge of his nose for closer inspection. She said, "Sweetheart," and without missing a beat he replied, "Yes, darling." She added, "Our first stop will be in Cabo San Lucas, then we'll go to Puerto Vallarta, Mazatlan, Ixtapa, and Acapulco." Guy immediately started singing a Mexican classic ballad entitled, 'La Paloma', as if to toast their trip with a song. In the end, everything was reduced to music with him. I was somewhat shocked that Marianne was able to convince him to get on a big ship, but he was always surprising me.

"Robaire," Guy said mischievously, "What will you be doing while your mother and I are 'cruising'?" When he said the word 'cruising', he put his nose up in the air like a snob just to crack us up, and the effect worked. I was laughing especially hard.

When Guy got me alone he cracked me up again saying, "Haitians and boats just do not mix Robaire. You've seen the news showing two hundred Haitians on a homemade raft floating to Miami? But I will do it for your mother because she is very excited about spending New Years Eve on a ship."

Marianne called out to Guy, "Sweetheart, don't forget your passport and your O-1 visa." Oh how his eyes lit up whenever he heard 'O-1 visa'.

"Robaire," I do not know one other Haitian who can cross borders as freely as I can with this visa you secured for me. Thank you again, my son."

Guy and Marianne's eyes lit up brightly as they closed the door of the cab that had driven them from the San Diego airport down to the pier where the Princess cruise ship awaited them in the bay. It was enormous, larger even than Guy could have ever imagined. He looked at Marianne and said, "Rich country." She giggled at him and took his hand comfortably into hers, pleased with her lover's boyish exuberance. She was relieved at his reaction to the ship because she suspected that Guy was reluctantly taking this cruise with her just to make her happy, and deep inside she knew it would be something that they would both never forget. He was so spoilable because of his own selflessness and his willingness to truly please her. If Guy was anywhere near his love, he was touching her, massaging her feet, pulling her closer to him and kissing her face tenderly, the way that Marianne always knew was possible but had nearly conceded to a routine marriage. She beamed while approaching the ship, knowing that they both deserved to be spoiled for the next ten days.

Cabo San Lucas was gorgeous, as was the entire Baja peninsula, although Guy and Marianne decided to stay on board the ship that day and relax. The first evening had been eventful as they both dressed up for dinner, Guy in a suit and tie, Marianne in a lovely evening gown. They both loved to get dressed up and make a grand impression, and that is exactly what they did at dinner. Seated around the oval table from them were four other couples from all over the United States. One of the men was a business owner, another couple was a husband and wife real estate sales team, still another couple was retired, and all of them were very nice indeed. On the third night of the cruise things were becoming a bit more familiar at the dinner table and Guy and Marianne began to make friends with the couple seated next to them.

Donna and her husband Phil asked Guy, "What do you do for a living, Guy?"

"I am a conductor and arranger and I have done some film scoring."

Marianne leapt right in after Guy, "Guy is a wonderful entertainer. He's an internationally recognized musician." She was so proud of him. Guy was lucky that the darkness of his skin wouldn't betray his blushing. In no time, the entire table was buzzing about Guy and there was a suggestion that he perform sometime during the cruise. One of the couples seconded the motion, saying, "You could perform in the ship's theater at the amateur contest, Guy!" Guy masterfully hid his disdain at the mention of his name and amateur in the same sentence and humbly answered instead, "I could never distract from another's performance, that wouldn't be professional." They got the hint, but Guy and Marianne's shipmates wouldn't let it go as they peppered the waiter with questions about the availability of another piano on board the ship somewhere. The waiter signaled the concierge to their table to discuss the possibility of freeing up a piano for Guy to perform on. The concierge was a young man in his early forties and he was of Columbian descent, smartly dressed and very articulate. When told of Guy's prowess, he got pensive for a moment then smiled at Guy saying, "I know who you are, Mr. duRosier. You have performed in Colombia years ago, have you not?" Guy answered him affirmatively in perfect Spanish that he had indeed lived in Bogotá for years and had a weekly variety show there and did some film scoring as well. After they finished their conversation in Spanish, the concierge gushed to the rest of the table, "I can assure you that this man, Maestro Guy duRosier, is a magnificent musician and I will do my best to locate a piano for you to play sir."

Guy bowed his head, "Gracias señor, muy amable."

The table was abuzz with the confirmation and they all were eager to hear Guy perform. Guy whispered into Marianne's ear, "It's good to be wanted in the Pacific darling." She giggled at him, her eyes twinkling with pride for her lover. They were the center of attention at their dinner table, on this monstrous ship, out in the middle of the Pacific Ocean, where Guy was expecting anonymity, but finding instead that his charisma knew no borders.

The next morning they docked in the bay in Puerto Vallarta where they decided to set out on their own rather than pay for the guided tours, because Guy spoke Spanish so well that they could get around just fine on their own. They decided that they would meet up later with Donna and Phil, their dinner mates, at the Westin hotel, where they had a timeshare, but first they wanted to walk around and go to the outdoor market. The rust-colored cobblestone street was lined with taco vendors, and children selling Chiclets gum alongside the wondrous beauty of the ocean. It struck Guy sadly, a cruel reminder of the deprivation in his own country, and Marianne saw the anguish wash over his face at the sight of three year old children selling gum for money. Much like Haiti, the beauty of the place couldn't hide, try as it might, the degradation of its people. Guy reached into his pocket and pulled out a five-dollar bill to hand to a pretty little girl in a white lace dress. She wore white patent leather shoes with her dress and looked like she belonged in church, not out soliciting so that her family could have a little cash for food. Her eyes lit up at the sight of the five- dollar bill and she quickly took hold of it knowing that if left dangling for long someone would snatch it out of the air. Soon Guy was besieged with children putting out their hands until he emptied his pockets of his cash. Marianne was struck by the pained expression on his face and simultaneously comforted by his sensitivity. She knew that she had herself a sweet, sweet man and he knew that he would have been dead four years ago without her. She felt her pulse beat strong while holding his hand. Just like lovers do. She couldn't tell at first if it was her pulse beating in her hand or his pulse that she was feeling. But she could feel it all over her body, in her hand, her heart, and her head, intoxicating her with every beat, and this was what people always raved about…chemistry. They were high school sweethearts, walking down a cobblestone street in Puerto Vallarta, Mexico and how they ever got here, at this moment, after such a long separation from their meeting in Harrison Hot Springs, was beyond comprehension. They both knew that they were the exception that confirms the rule. They were given a second chance at love.

Guy saw a pair of Bostonian shoes that he just had to have, regardless of the fit. "They look too tight, sweetheart," Marianne said to Guy. "No darling, they are fine," he answered back. Ever since I had given Guy a pair of my Bostonian shoes to wear, he was hooked and would only buy Bostonians. "These are real Republican shoes, Robaire," he beamed. The price was ridiculously low in Mexico so he was going to fit into those shoes no matter what. Marianne grinned to herself as her lover walked ever so gingerly in his skin-tight Bostonians. They were right on schedule to meet Donna and Phil at the Westin Hotel for some relaxation beside the pool before boarding the ship. When Guy came out of the bathroom in his bathing suit, Marianne was thrilled to see him in a pair of shorts because with all of her travels to the Bahamas, she had never seen Guy don a pair of shorts once. She had on an elegant blue one-piece and was just finishing up applying a liberal amount of sunscreen to protect her skin as Guy sat beside her and their shipmates on the pool deck. The pool was masterfully designed so that when you were swimming, you couldn't tell where the pool water ended and the ocean began. It gave the appearance of flowing right into the ocean. "Are you going to join me in here, Guy?" Marianne teased. She had never seen Guy in the water and frankly didn't even know if he could swim. Several times in Nassau, she had asked him to go to the beach with her and he would go, but he always sat inside of the parked car reading or writing music while she swam in the beautiful Caribbean ocean. Just then, Guy got up without answering her, slid past her down the stairs of the pool and swam off looking over his shoulder smiling at her all the while. "You didn't think black people could swim, did you darling?" Guy laughed. She laughed along with him, but she really was very surprised to see him frolicking in the water, so she swam after her man and caught up with him just in time to give him a big kiss. "I wouldn't put anything past you, sweetheart," she grinned as she held onto Guy, arms around his neck and weightless in the water. Guy's adoration for Marianne was always most evident in these moments. In the moments when Marianne lavished affection all over him, he smiled sheepishly like a little boy who had a crush on his schoolteacher and would do just about anything in the world for her. It began with a curling of the corner of his mouth into a grin, and his eyes lowered, almost afraid to make eye contact. Then, he would summon his courage to look directly into her pretty blue eyes, and his grin would morph into laughter at some riotously funny comment he would make, leaving the pair clinging to each other in laughter. This was the glue that bound Guy and Marianne and it was also the antidote to any grief or stress that attempted to invade their charmed environment. Marianne knew that they were the envy of every mature couple, as she need only observe people's looks of longing and envy at their love for one another. She knew they practically walked on air together and it was obvious to everyone else too.

"Is it time to go back to the behemoth, darling," Guy questioned? They were enjoying themselves so much in Puerto Vallarta that they hated to leave, but the ship was headed out again and they looked forward to seeing Acapulco next. That evening at dinner, the concierge stopped by the table to inform Guy that he had indeed secured a piano for his use whenever he would like to play. As he offered Marianne her choice of desserts, he said to Guy, "It's located on the third floor, behind the theater, Monsieur duRosier, and I would love to attend any performance you may give, sir." Guy thanked him, but looked hesitant to accept the invitation, ever careful to be humble, and never making the mistake of seeming too hungry for the spotlight. The bright lights always found Guy without his ever looking for it. His dinner mates sensed his hesitation and Donna, with whom Marianne had made fast friends, urged her to convince Guy to play even if it was only for their table. Marianne looked at Donna with a twinkle in her eye, saying, "I'll get him to play, don't worry." The next evening, Marianne announced that Guy would play the piano when everyone returned from the day trip to Acapulco. This delighted the table and someone seated across from Guy asked, "Do you mind if we invite some other people as well, Guy?" Guy, ever so shyly deferred to Marianne as if he didn't understand the question posed him, feigning a lack of understanding of English. He knew well what was being said, but he loved to defer to Marianne when all eyes were upon him. This fake shyness served him very well, even creating a veil of mystery around him. Marianne nodded in the affirmative and answered, "Certainly, you can invite whomever you like. Guy is used to performing in front of large audiences around the world."

Many of the movies of the sixties and early seventies as well as the weekly program, 'Wide World of Sports,' had put Acapulco on the map because of its cliff diving. And this was the first thing that Guy and Marianne wanted to see in Acapulco. Guy negotiated with the cab driver in Spanish and before they knew it, they were at a nice restaurant up on top of the cliffs, looking out at the beautiful ocean below. The thin, deeply tanned young men stood within twenty or thirty feet of their table, offering a magnificent view of the diving taking place right before their eyes. The divers carefully fashioned a toe-hold on the edge of the cliff, then stood patiently with arms raised over their heads waiting for just the right moment when the wind was negligible and all seemed suitable for this leap into a tiny crevice of water, hundreds of feet below. Guy and Marianne held hands tightly, feeling nervous themselves for these courageous young divers they were watching. With a deep knee bend and a violent push up and out, chest extended and arms out wide, the young man made like a bird in front of the entire lunch crowd. These were professional divers. They were paid next to nothing by the restaurant owners to provide this entertainment, and Marianne was astonished to think that these men would put their lives at risk for a few pesos. When one of the divers came by their table, this time it was Marianne who reached into her pocket to tip the brave young man.

That evening, back on the ship it was show time for Guy. He expected to play a few songs for the five or ten people who had grown to know him and Marianne over the course of the cruise, but when they arrived they were surprised to see a big crowd of people gathered around the piano. He performed his routine, 'Around the World,' wherein he announced the country and sang a classic song from that country in its native tongue. First, he started with Spain, then Brazil, then Mexico, which was a big hit as they were on a Mexican cruise, then Haiti, then a number from West Side Story, even a Japanese classic, then a German song as well. When he finished his forty-five minute set, Donna knew immediately why Guy didn't perform at the amateur night contest. The crowd clapped enthusiastically, then asked Guy to perform another song and he obliged. The first person to make their way to Guy was a Mexican woman who was just awestruck by his ability to sing her favorite Mexican song. Then, one by one, their dinner mates all came over to thank Guy for his performance calling it the highlight of their trip. He had indeed helped to make the last evening of the cruise a memorable one for everybody. Back inside of their cabin, Guy and Marianne enjoyed a cigarette together and kicked their heels up, content to spend the last evening relaxing with chocolate and cigarettes, their shared little guilty pleasures. "Darling," Guy asked, "What do you suppose our beloved son is doing?" "You miss Robert, don't you sweetheart?" she replied. He answered, "Immensely." She continued, "You know Guy, Robert is absolutely crazy about you." Guy grinned, "Me too." What Guy saw in me was him- self thirty years ago, and he was committed to making his relationship with Marianne and me one of the few enduring relationships of his lifetime. Like a fish that swims

wherever the current takes it, Guy never had an opportunity to culti-
vate close, lasting relationships because the requirements of his chosen
profession called for him to chase the gig, wherever that may take him,
and take him it did to several continents. Guy mused further, "Darling,
the conversations that Robaire and I have are so intellectual. He is an
intellectual young man, you know?" She nodded in agreement. "And
he is always so willing to please me. What a son! It's a good thing he
is so big, because his sensitivity and his candor make him so fragile."
Guy finished, "Yes my Anne-Marie, I adore that child." "Well, you'll be
able to see him tomorrow and get caught up on everything. You two
should start planning your next CD." Before she knew it, Guy was fast
asleep and she took the time to think about her life together with him
and how much it had changed from the mundane to the exciting. She
watched him sleep just like she had when they first met in Vancouver,
B. C. thirty-three years ago. She was proud of herself for having the
courage to leave everything behind and start a new life with her lover.
Passion and desire were now a part of her vocabulary, and a part of her
life everyday. She was also proud to be able to show her son that his
mother and father were in love. This was never the objective to begin
with, but the fact that it turned out this way just made everything perfect. She draped one arm lightly over Guy's chest, tucked her chin just
over his shoulder and fell asleep content, knowing that he had really
enjoyed himself on the cruise.

I picked the 'cruisers' up at the airport and I immediately sensed that
they had a great time judging from the big smile on Marianne's face
and the 'confident, almost cocky' way that Guy was sauntering off of
the airplane in his new, too-tight, Bostonian shoes. Guy's right arm was
draped over Marianne's shoulder lovingly and she was tucked up in his
shoulder like a little ball. "There is our hero, little girl," Guy exclaimed
as he pointed in my direction. He loved calling Marianne his 'little girl',
and she adored it as well. After receiving kisses from both of them, we
loaded the baggage in the car and Guy started raving about the cruise
saying, "I had no idea that cruising could be so much fun Robaire. I'll
never question your mother's judgment ever again." Marianne was
beaming. "Robert, your papa had the time of his life on that ship." I
laughed, recalling his joke about Haitians and boats not mixing too
well. Looking into the rear view mirror sent shivers of happiness down
my spine as my mother and father were cuddling together, necking

while I was driving them home. I had come so very, very, far from my moments of despair and there was no blueprint that I followed, no road map or travel book: I simply had fashioned my own idea of what family should be in my mind, and it was all manifesting itself before my very eyes. One of the great marvels of human consciousness is that whatever situation we can clearly perceive, we improve. The moment that change became an absolute necessity in my life, my life changed. The undeniable proof was in my rear view mirror, and when I looked at it out of the corner of my eye, I was a changed man.

16

C'EST LA VIE

"Hello, This is Mr. Bob Neree calling for Guy duRosier, please," I heard as I held the receiver to my ear. "This is his son, Robert," I answered. "You can leave a message with me or reach Guy at this number," I added. He said, "Robert, I am the editor of a National publication called 'Haitienne Aujourdhui', with circulation in Haiti, Paris, Montreal, Martinique, New York, Miami, Boston, Washington, D. C., and Chicago, among other places, and I'd like to fly out to Seattle to do a cover story on your father." I knew that Guy would love to do the story and I related my sentiments to Mr. Neree before repeating Guy's telephone number to him and saying goodbye. I immediately picked up the phone and dialed Guy, sensing a fantastic opportunity to market his last recording, 'Reminiscences Haitiennes' at the national level, through the magazine. Marianne answered the phone and sounded either distracted or concerned, I wasn't certain which. "Robert, I had to take your father to see Dr. Anderson this morning because he's been having bad headaches for a while now and last night he fell against the wall in the hallway, knocking a picture off of the wall." I straightened up in my chair, "Is he all right Mom?" "Well, Dr. Anderson thinks from a preliminary examination that it is just the flu, but your father says he has never had the flu in his life. He insists it is not the flu." I sobered even further and asked Marianne to have him call me when he woke up.

"My son, how doing," Guy asked in his broken English, charmingly leaving out the 'are', and the 'you' in his greeting. "I'm cool papa, but I hear you have the flu or something," I questioned. "Let me tell you Robaire," he said. "I am having some headaches man." He really emphasized the word 'headaches' by taking his voice up an octave and slowly saying the word. I knew exactly what he meant when he did that. It meant he was serious. I had never heard him complain in the five years that I had now known him. He changed the subject quickly by telling me that he had spoken with Bob Neree about the magazine article and just as I had hoped, he agreed that it was a marketing dream come true for the disc we had recorded in Haiti. He said, "I agreed to be on the cover provided he would insert a half page advertisement of our CD inside." "What did he say to that papa?" "My son," he smiled, "He is flying here from New York next week to interview me."

Marianne was still tanned from the cruise when she called me over to tell me privately that she was concerned about Guy and the pain he was having from his headaches. She had every reason to be concerned, I knew, because she had watched him suffer two seizures in five years, one in Nassau, Bahamas and the other in Seattle, both of them grand mal seizures that required his hospitalization. In addition, he had been pistol whipped at the Buena Vista restaurant in Nassau and hospitalized with a concussion. She had every reason to be concerned and I asked her quickly if there was anything that I could do to be of help. "Your father has been suffering from severe headaches for about two weeks now, Robert and it has gotten to the point where he is sleeping on the sofa so that he doesn't wake me up. I don't think he is sleeping at all because the pain is so intense, but it is hard to tell with your dad because he just is not a complainer at all." She moved closer to me, not wanting Guy to hear her whisper, "Robert, your father fell over on top of me the other day. I was fortunate to be in his way, otherwise he would have probably fallen face-first to the floor. It was all I could do to keep him upright." I felt my insides churning, agonizing, while my head got light from working overtime trying to make what Marianne was saying go away. I sensed trouble not only because of the facts she gave me but mostly from the grave look on her face. She whispered, "Can you come get him tomorrow and take him to the hospital just to have them do some precautionary testing?" "Sure mom, I'll come over and pick him up in the morning then take him to Evergreen Hospital." I tried in vain to eliminate the worst-case scenarios from my mind on the drive back home, reasoning that he couldn't be epileptic because he had already been tested for that. I had remembered hearing of a professional baseball player who missed a whole season due to vertigo and

wondered if the symptoms that were manifesting in Guy were indica-
tive of such. One thing I knew for sure was that it would be no picnic
at all trying to convince Guy to go to the hospital. He hated going
to doctors and everything associated with it, including the shots and
x-rays, but his phobia had certainly softened some since his friend-
ship with Dr. Anderson and the subsequent maintenance of his high
blood pressure problem. He was skeptical of western medicine, particularly prescription pills, until his high blood pressure problem was
completely eradicated by Dr. Anderson. "Robaire," he raved, "My high
blood pressure is gone and Dr. Anderson gives me free pills to main-
tain my perfect blood pressure. Science is too much, Robaire. I'll stick
to dissecting harmony and leave the protons and neutrons to the men
in white coats." He said something else about Louis Pasteur being the
father of modern medicine just to let me know that he knew a little
something about the subject. Guy loved to reference the father of any
particular school of thought, whether it was Copernicus and astrology,
Socrates, Aristotle, or Plato and philosophy, and now he was laying Dr.
Louis Pasteur on me out of nowhere. He needn't ever impress me and
he wasn't trying, but there was something about being from a 'Third
World' country that prompted Guy to let me know he had an entirely
'First World' mind, capable of holding his own with the most scholarly
of thinkers. I recalled shortly after meeting Guy, telling him that I had
graduated from Arizona State University with a degree in Economics
and he smiled saying, "Ah my son, so you are 'lettered' in Economics?"
Without hesitation he asked me, "Do you adhere to the precepts of
Milton Friedman or Keynes?" He added before I could answer, "I prefer monetarism over fiscal policy." After I picked my chin up off of the
floor, I smiled at Guy saying, "You are too, too much Papa." I knew that
comparisons were a futile, wasted effort, still I could not help but wonder what I may have been capable of had I been subject to my father's
influence over the course of an entire childhood and lifetime. He had
a phenomenal capacity for abstract thought and I knew that I had it
too. However, I couldn't get out of my mind, as hard as I tried, images
of Ivo Bannister coming home from Boeing and taking off his steel-
toed boots, picking the metal shavings out of his coveralls, grabbing
a cold beer out of the fridge, and reclining in his chair to watch 'The
Flintstones' cartoons until he fell asleep. I was never one to dwell on the
past or on comparisons though, so I instead chose to bridge the gap of

these two polar opposites by concentrating on the positive at all times. To answer his question, I said, "I'm a monetarist papa. Less government and taxation can only spur reinvestment into our economy, creating more jobs and causing a trickle-down effect on the economy." "You are your father's son," Guy beamed with pride. We had these types of conversations on a regular basis whether it was religion, politics, music, or philosophy and we were always in agreement.

The next morning I arrived early in hopes of getting Guy into and out of the emergency room at Evergreen Hospital in a reasonable amount of time. Nothing moved quickly in a hospital but I hoped for a quick examination and then we'd be out of there and on the golf course by about noon. Guy was not at all pleased about going to the hospital for a headache.

"Robaire, sometimes your mother is too sober. All I need is a little Thera-Flu and I will be fine, man," he said.

I understood his reluctance but sided with Marianne, knowing how concerned she was about his health. "We'll just go get you checked out and be out on the golf course in no time Papa." He immediately cheered up over that.

After about ten minutes we were led into an examination room and Guy was asked to roll his shirtsleeves up so the doctor could take his blood pressure. Next, he was asked a series of questions about his headaches, and Guy downplayed each inquiry, admitting to just a little bit of pain towards the front of his head. After nearly being released, the doctor stood with his hand under his chin thinking to himself for a moment then said, "Just to be on the safe side, I'd like to take a CT-scan of your chest, Mr. duRosier." I explained to Guy what that was, and he agreed, quickly moving his body into position in between two heavy steel panels that were placed at his chest and back in the exact same position. A radiology technician came into the room and asked Guy to remain as still as possible for the next minute or so, and he did just that until the technician returned to the room and repositioned the panels for one more x-ray. We waited in the room for about the next ten minutes, giving the doctor time to interpret the x-rays and return to the room where Guy and I sat laughing about some joke he made regarding technology. The doctor returned to the room and solemnly started in on his interpretation of the CT-scan, saying, "Mr. duRosier, from what I see here," and he pointed at two smallish brown nodules,

"I am concerned about these two nodules because they have a propensity to indicate something that is originating in your lung and traveling to your liver, and even possibly to your lymph nodes. In my opinion, this is alarming enough for me to strongly recommend that you have a magnetic resonance imaging scan, or MRI, performed right away so that we can find out for sure what is going on here." Guy looked at me and sighed, knowing we weren't going to be teeing off at Willows golf course anytime soon. "Papa, I think that this is something you should have done as soon as possible," I said, and Guy answered, "Whatever you think is best, Robaire." The doctor said that the room was currently open and that he could get in right away, so we started heading that way. The doctor alarmed me even further when he asked who Guy's primary care provider was because he wanted him to come out to the hospital and bring Guy's medical charts and to help him review the results of his MRI. This was all a bit more than I expected to encounter on this beautiful May morning.

I waited outside the room knowing that it would take about forty minutes, because I had been through an MRI before when I discovered I had two herniated discs in my back. The hallway was long and carpeted so I sat down and rested my back against the brick wall behind me and looked at the beautiful prints on the wall portraying what looked to be Hawaii or the Caribbean, I wasn't sure which. We were in a remote section of the hospital now, so there was very little traffic going back or forth allowing me to sit and daydream about my upcoming trip to Hawaii, and about our next recording that Guy and I had started developing ideas for. His last recording, 'Reminiscences Haitiennes,' was deliberately titled Volume I, so that we could follow that up with Volume II, three of the songs for which Guy had already written. I continued to sit with both knees bent, tapping out a Creole tune and using my legs for percussion, when the door to the MRI room opened slowly and Dr. Anderson emerged. I stood up and saw him approach me tentatively. He was one of the few people I knew who stood taller than I, at about six feet four inches, so when he came within a couple of feet from me, we looked at each other directly, eye to eye. What I saw when I looked into Dr. Timothy Anderson's kind eyes made my heart stop beating momentarily and my throat stick, making it impossible to swallow. What I saw was tears forming and dropping from the corner of his right eye, then falling down his cheek quickly as he removed his glasses and brushed the side of his face dry with the sleeve of his white medical coat. I was frozen in place getting myself ready to reject whatever horrible thing it was that reduced this sweet man to tears on my father's behalf. "Robert," he whispered. "Your dad has got over seven cancerous tumors. It has originated in his lungs, spread to his liver, into his lymph nodes and finally metastasizing on his brain. He has a large tumor on his frontal lobe which is directly responsible for his balance problems and headaches." Now I couldn't see him through my tears and I couldn't feel the weight of my body either, but I listened to him finish these agonizing words that were burning my ears. "Because the cancer has spread already to his lymph nodes, we cannot stop it at this point. Chemotherapy would be useless and only subject him to extreme sickness. To regain some balance we can give him a series of twenty one radiation therapy visits that should effectively reduce the size of his largest tumor and enable him to regain some of his balance." Now I was dying; so much for my vertigo theory. I was in pain. Dr. Anderson finished even more softly and sadly, saying, "Robert, Guy has only got about sixty to ninety days to live, and that is our best-case scenario." I collapsed against the brick wall, falling sideways into it, my head spinning around and around until I crumpled into a ball on the floor, hugging my knees to my chest and sobbing. "No, no, no, no, no, no, no," I whimpered rocking myself back and forth as Dr. Anderson tried to help me to my feet. "I can call your mother and talk to her if you'd like me to, Robert," Dr. Tim said. He added, "Guy will need to stay here indefinitely for now." I told God, whom I had always relied on and never questioned in my entire life, that he just wasn't fair and that he should take me too. Then I remembered Mother Theresa's words, "Love until it hurts. Real love is always painful and hurts; then it is real and pure."

At the same time that I was agonizing over Guy's condition, Marianne stood in the hallway of Fairfax Hospital where she worked as a dietician, talking to one of the nurses about Guy. I had phoned her at work after his CT scan and given her the news that the doctor was recommending an MRI because of the suspicious nodules. After Marianne relayed the physical evidence to the nurse, the nurse told her that it was the worst possible news and that Guy likely had a very short time to live. The nurse did not know the nature of Marianne's relationship to Guy, so she very bluntly told Marianne that he would probably only live a few months. Tears always came easily to Marianne's eyes, but this was something different, something agonizing that caught her from the stomach and stripped her of all of the joy that was so easily contained in her very spirit. The luster in her blue eyes was instantly gone and the optimism in her step, lively as could be, was forever changed as she walked slowly, deliberately back down the hall toward the kitchen. She was Guy's 'little girl' and she feared a future without him would turn her literally into his nickname for her. She was at once sad and afraid like a little girl but she gathered herself enough to finish her shift and drive directly to the hospital. She searched her memory for any hint that could have tipped her off to Guy's condition sooner but found none. She realized that his performance on the cruise ship may very well end up being his last and she was saddened deeply.

That night Guy rested comfortably in his hospital room and brightened considerably when he saw his Anne-Marie, his little girl walking sadly into the room. She put her head on his chest and cried while he said, "Darling, don't cry, it's only a little cancer." He tried valiantly to lighten the mood saying, "They tell me I have cancer but I say that cancer has me." With that statement he laughed so hard that he nearly fell out of the bed, then Marianne and I laughed with him. I was astonished at his levity and proud of his courage in the face of such news. He then looked at me saying, "Robaire, I don't have cancer, I am cancer!" We laughed hard again and I knew that my Papa was going to be just fine. What a man! He didn't yet know the doctor's consensus on his prognosis for life expectancy, and he looked at cancer like it was a cold that he could whip with the proper rest and maybe some bush medicine from Billy and Shoe back in the Bahamas.

I left Guy and Marianne alone for a bit to go talk with Dr. Anderson about my scheduled trip to Maui, and he convinced me that there was no imminent danger to Guy over the course of the next ten days, "However," he cautioned, "He is in serious condition that can worsen overnight Robert." I went back inside the hospital room to witness the love birds cuddling up together on Guy's bed, and I told Guy that I was going to Hawaii for ten days but that I would check in with him every day to ensure that he was doing okay. "Papa," I said, "Your 'little girl' will take great care of you while I'm gone and I want you to promise me that you'll be ready to go golfing by the time I get back. "Okay, Robaire," he whispered weakly.

Marianne had only recently been granted a leave of absence from her job due to an on the job injury that was diagnosed as a 'frozen shoulder', so she was able and willing to spend time with Guy at the hospital until he could be released. I didn't believe in coincidences ever since meeting my angel, Ethel St. Claire, in the Miami airport, and I didn't think it was a coincidence that Marianne would be granted an extended time off of work at the same time that Guy became ill and needed to be cared for.

Before leaving, I said to Marianne, "Mom, here's the phone numbers of the hotels where I will be staying. I'll be at the Kea Lani in Maui for seven days, then the Sheraton in Waikiki for three days. Call me if there is an emergency." I kissed her on the cheek and gave her a big hug. "I'm glad you're here to take care of papa," I smiled. Everywhere I went in my car for the next day or two before leaving, I listened to Miriam Makeba, the prolific African singer, and Gilberto Gil, a Brazilian singer, and I couldn't stop crying. I had begun to grieve the eventual loss of Guy and it was devastating to my psyche. I couldn't believe I could only have him for five years. I was just beginning to get my feet on the ground and understand who and what I was, something so different from my orientation in the Bannister household. I was estranged from Ivo and Ione Bannister for five years, ever since they made the racial comment that was unacceptable, and Marianne was alone in her own grief for her lover, leaving me somewhat isolated from her emotionally as well, thus, that old, familiar, dreaded sense of isolation from the world was back at my doorstep again, knocking ever so loudly, and I wanted to put my hands over my ears to make it stop. Molly, my wonderful caseworker, and symbol of hope, would have held onto my hand tightly if she were here, making the knots in my stomach loosen some. Where was my little friend, my warrior who guided me through life until I no longer needed him? I wondered if he would come back to me now, or if he had forsaken me for some other child who needed him worse. My plea was answered when words of comfort began swirling around my head. Strength is found with self control; mastery comes from right thought; calmness is power; be still my heart.

"The first radiation treatment is always the worst, Marianne, but I can assure you that Guy will become less and less affected by the radiation as we progress through his series," said the radiologist to Marianne, trying his best to calm her down after she saw how violently sick Guy was. He couldn't stop throwing up and she just hated to see her sweetheart ill this way. He was so vibrant, so radiant on stage, and such a serene man off of it, that to see him this way was nearly intolerable to her. Even in his agony, Guy was stoic, telling Marianne, "God is good to let me have you darling." She tipped her head to one side, the way she did when she was especially touched, and blinked through a lovely smile for Guy. She wondered what she would ever do without him and prayed secretly that if he had to go, for God to spare him leaving on her birthday. She calculated the time that Dr. Anderson had given Guy to live and feared the proximity to her birthday.

The surgery room was quiet when Guy's doctor entered to do a biopsy on the nodule located on his lung. However, it wasn't quiet for long, as Guy's lung collapsed during the biopsy, requiring a trip to the intensive care unit. Meanwhile, Marianne was downstairs in the hospital room wondering what was taking so long. The first hour was reasonable, but by now two hours had gone by when she finally asked the nurses what was going on with Guy. She was taken upstairs to a room in intensive care where she slept with Guy, unable to sleep really because of the bubbling sound that the lung machine emitted constantly. Guy slept like a baby though, because he was so doped up that he didn't hear or feel a thing. After two days waiting for the lung to re-inflate, the doctor decided that he would have to do it via an injection with a long needle. This was a last resort because he mentioned to Marianne that it is one of the most painful things to have to endure, but at this point, he was left with no choice. He said, "This is going to be extremely painful for Guy but there is an agent in the shot itself that will cause him to have no memory of it." "Oh dear," said Marianne with her hand covering her mouth. Next, she had to watch in horror as Guy writhed in agony as a long needle was inserted into his chest to try and reinflate his lung. "This is going to be very painful for a moment Guy, then the pain will subside," the doctor warned. Guy was the definition of composure in his life, but composure was impossible just now and Marianne could only shake her head back and forth and cry because her lovely man was out of his head with pain. She wished she could take the pain away, knowing that someone as sweet as her Guy should never have to endure what she was seeing. The first attempt did not re-inflate the lung and he was subjected to a second injection without anesthesia. Marianne now wept openly. Her man was full of needles and tubes, hooked to machines, and lay writhing in pain when the next indignity arrived. Guy needed a catheter hooked up and he didn't understand what they were doing to him, pleading with Marianne in French to make

them stop. She couldn't understand his French, but she knew that he was very disconcerted by the catheter. He did not want this done. Finally, three nurses had to restrain him, tying his arms to the sides of the bedposts for his own good. Marianne couldn't believe what was happening. It was only a few days ago that Guy was seemingly fine, aside from his headaches. Now the world was different and getting worse every minute. Finally, his lung had re-inflated and he was stabilizing, asking the nurses if they would 'untie him'. "Darling, do they really tie you to the bed in a first world country?" Guy reasoned with Marianne, clearly regaining his composure and sense of humor just in time to save her from her own heart attack. "They had to, sweetheart, because you were trying to pull your catheter out and that would have been so, so painful for you. They didn't mean any harm, they were just trying to keep you from hurting yourself." Guy petitioned, "I'm cool now darling. Can they untie my arms?" Marianne beat him to the punch by getting up while he was asking and going to the nurse's station to ask on his behalf if they would free up his arms. He was too dignified for this, she knew, and she sensed he had calmed down enough not to be of any harm to himself. "Will you please take the arm restraints off of Guy, now," she begged the nurse. She answered, "Yes, provided you're certain he won't try to pull out the catheter again." Marianne assured her, "He won't. I've talked with him about it." The nurse came into the room and quickly took the restraints off of Guy and he thanked her for doing so. Then he smiled at Marianne saying, "Thank you, little girl."

Marianne had been spending the nights with Guy and most of the days as well, going home briefly just to shower and get caught up with her mail and pay bills, logistical things, then return promptly back to her love. Guy was a third of the way through his radiation treatments and was regaining a little balance but still not enough to guarantee his equilibrium was intact, but to him the slight improvement led him to believe he was healed. Therefore, when Marianne informed him he could not yet leave the hospital, Guy was disconsolate. He slept uneasily that evening like Marianne had been each and every night. She heard him stir in his bed but she went back to sleep until she heard a loud crash and saw that Guy was no longer in his bed, while his intravenous tubes hung disconnected, dangling in mid-air. She leapt out of her chair and circled around the foot of the bed to find Guy lying prone on the ground, face down, with a pool of blood forming under his right eye. "Oh my god," Marianne shouted and ran out to locate the evening nurse on duty. Guy had fallen directly face first onto the concrete hospital room floor in his haste to get out of there, thinking his balance was just fine. Instead, he had fifty-seven stitches sewn over his right eye to close the gash, and to go with that he had seven tumors, and a collapsed lung. Marianne could take no more as she had to watch Guy be restrained yet again, and she met privately with one of the nurses, asking, "Guy has a son who is vacationing in Hawaii, and a daughter in New York. Do you think I should call them to be here? Is he going to die?" She hated to say that word, but she had a responsibility to get as much of Guy's family around him as possible if it were true. She hoped the nurse would say "no", but she didn't. "Yes," the nurse said tersely, "I would do that if I were you."

The phone rang in my hotel room seven days into my vacation and it was Marianne. I took the phone out onto the deck and sat down on a lounge chair in the sun. "Robert, you're father is in very bad shape and I think you should be here." She proceeded to fill me in with all of the details and I couldn't believe my ears. What she said terrified me. I was so grateful that she was there with him and I didn't know how I could possibly see him that way. In a way, I was hiding from what I wanted to refuse to acknowledge, but I promised Marianne I would call her the next morning to get an update from her on Guy's health. The next morning she called me again and told me that Guy's eye had completely swollen shut and that it was turning black and blue. In short, he was a complete mess. "Okay mom, I'll check the loads out of here and get home on the first available flight." I had traveled to Hawaii on a non-revenue pass through my airline job, meaning I didn't have to pay for the ticket, thus, I could only get home on a flight that had open seats after all of the paying passengers had boarded. The first flight I could get home on left the following day, so I got on and said my prayers all the way home.

Guy looked like he had been on the losing end of a prizefight with Mike Tyson, squinting up at me through a swollen eye socket and stitches just above his eyebrow. Luckily, I found a parking space outside of the hospital doors where I could put my shoulder around Guy and walk him inside the automatic glass doors where a wheelchair sat waiting for us to use. Guy had been allowed to go home with Marianne days earlier, and I was picking him up and taking him to his last few radiation treatments. He could only take a few steps on his own without teetering on the brink of falling over in any direction. It was a long way to the radiology center as I wheeled Guy down a blue corridor to a red corridor then green. My color-blindness problem didn't work well with these corridors, but Guy knew the way since he had been this route about fourteen times already. As we took our final left turn and rolled towards the radiology department, shouts of "Hi, Guy," floated our direction. He had done it again. The radiologists all loved Guy already and were on a first name basis, even taking time to joke with him. Guy joked back with them saying, "Is the Sacred Beast ready for me?" This was his nick-name for the huge machine that looked like a telephone receiver that rotated around his head as he lay prone while the radiologists lined up the lasers to the exact point on his brain where the largest tumor was located. "Yeah Guy, the Beast was just wondering where you were," said Mike, one of the radiologists assembled outside of the room where another person had wheeled Guy. They took a moment to introduce themselves to me, showing me the room and exactly how the treatment was performed. I went over to where Guy was lying and said, "Papa, you call this thing the Sacred Beast? You are so funny, man." It was imposing indeed, this giant telephone receiver, as it whirred into position quietly above Guy's head. Then the lasers came into place from both sides of the room, lining up directly on the tumor. Two thin red beams of light shimmered across the room to attack this insidious invader called cancer that I was acquiring a very serious hatred for. My generation had become diluted with fear of and respect for the disease called AIDS, however, I was getting acquainted with an equally disastrous disease called cancer. It was shredding weight off of Guy by the moment, leaving him with a skeletal look that left his skin dangling loosely from his now all too visible bone structure. I talked Guy into shaving his head, and Marianne shaved it leaving him looking quite fashionable as I explained to him that since Michael Jordan had started shaving his head bald, most black men were doing it as well, making it quite contemporary.

Outside of the radiology room I waited alongside Mike while Guy received his five or ten minute treatment. Mike said, "Your dad talks often about getting back out onto the golf course to play a round, Robert. Barring some miracle though, I just don't see that happening because we can only reduce the swelling on his brain enough to alleviate his painful headaches. His balance will get better, but I was telling him about this video golf game that he could play." I said, "Yeah, he loves to play golf, but I don't see how either because he has to lean on me just to walk."

After Guy's final treatment, he said farewell to the beast first, then to the radiology staff, and they all wished him the best of luck. I wheeled him for the last time up and down the color-coded corridors of Evergreen Hospital in Kirkland, Washington, and we stopped up at the information desk next to the exit doors where we always left the wheelchair before exiting together, my arm snugly around Guy's waist.

The middle of summer in Seattle could never come quickly enough simply because we were behind the rest of the nation's summer by about two months, so finally well into July, we actually could feel the heat for the first time. It seemed miraculous what I was watching that hot summer day, as Guy was teeing his ball up at the local driving range and swinging very carefully at his ball, sending it directly towards the 150-yard marker with regularity. He was not driving the ball like usual because he had to keep his feet planted firmly in the same spot. His balance was precarious at best, but Marianne and I decided to grant him his daily wish. He was so eager to get out and swing his clubs. I stood as close as I could to him without putting myself in danger of being clubbed by his back swing, still I could lunge after him and keep him from falling at the distance I kept. I took several photos of his swing just to remember that he was actually able to do it, and so that I could try to lift his spirits some. He was rejuvenated indeed, and on the way home we listened to our favorite CD by Gilberto Gil at the highest possible decibel that my speakers would stand. Listening to music together in my car was our communion together and we both really enjoyed it. The day was a huge success except for the one moment that I let my guard down thinking Guy was just fine. I walked beside Guy at Marianne's house and everywhere we went just so that he could reach out for me to collect his balance if need be, however, I listened to him when he said, "It's okay Robaire, I'm fine." He was so proud that he simply hated for me to have to walk side-by-side, so carefully watching his every step. I listened and walked in front of him only to feel the weight of his body suddenly careen into me, knocking me off balance and throwing him to the ground, cutting his knee badly enough to draw blood. I cursed myself, knowing I should not have listened to him and stayed right beside him, but I knew that from here on out, I would hold onto him whether he liked it or not.

It was getting harder and harder for me to visit Guy as July slid into August because he was deteriorating so rapidly. His weight loss was astounding, going from a healthy, athletic two hundred and five pounds down to about one hundred and sixty five pounds. Marianne explained to me that food just did not taste right to Guy, and when he had attempted to undertake a naturopathic diet in hopes of fending off the cancer, the food on his diet was horribly bland. "Darling," he grinned at Marianne, "Death could be favorable to this food." Marianne also informed me that Guy was beginning to hallucinate, seeing huge spiders on the walls and speaking to his mother Francine, who herself had passed away the previous year.

One afternoon, Guy looked unusually stoic to me, if not angry, when he called me into the living room and requested to speak to me in private. "Robaire," he questioned, "Why do you keep all of our compact discs at your house? How do I know that you are not selling them and keeping the money for yourself?" I was dumbfounded, shattered, and unable to respond to his question considering how my every effort since the moment I met him was made only in his best interest. He added, "You should bring all of the discs over here right away where I can keep an eye on them." I looked away from him for the first time in five years without feeling uplifted, responding, "Sure Papa, I'll have them here for you by tomorrow." I breezed by Marianne giving her a hug and left the house with tears in my eyes.

My phone was ringing at home minutes after my arrival. "Robert," Marianne said. "You have to know that your father is not in his right mind. Do not pay any attention at all to what he said to you." "But Mom," I protested, "Did you see how serious his face was when he said those things to me?" She reassured me, "I know, but you have to forget he ever said those things. You know better than anybody else how much he loves you." I said, "Yeah, you're right, Mom." She confided in me then, "He is seeing things and speaking Creole and French to me and sometimes to people who are not here. It really scares me when he sees the spiders." She went on, adding, "I've got to get some help over here from home hospice care nurses because I just can't do it by myself anymore. The other night your father took a bath and I couldn't get him out of the tub, and he didn't have any strength to lift himself out either. He was stuck in the tub, Robert, for close to an hour. I just didn't know what to do." I heard the desperation in her voice and it saddened me knowing what a difficult time she was having. "He can't go on my birthday Robert, I won't be able to take that." Finally, with her voice cracking and trailing off, she warned, "I want you to be able to be over here in a moment's notice Robert and be prepared to stay a few days because we could lose your father any time now." There it was out in the open. She had said it. I had to drop the veil of denial that I was clinging to and try to accept what was happening. For over a month, I had been unable to really sleep, choosing instead to go for long drives in the middle of the night, sometimes up to the Snoqualmie mountain pass and back, other times over one of the floating bridges that connects Seattle with the East side suburb where I lived. All the while I was crying and couldn't stop, sometimes so hard that I had to pull over on the side of the road for safety. I just couldn't figure life out and I didn't see how this was right or fair. At times I thought about confiding in Marianne but couldn't knowing that she was going through her own personal grief and not wanting to distract her from the wonderful job she was doing caring for Guy. The evening that I jumped the Skyline High School fence and sprinted around their track as fast as I could until I collapsed from exhaustion was the worst. I was having a very, very serious battle with despair the depth of which was intolerable. I loved this man so, so much that I couldn't accept a world without him and didn't know where my place would be in it. And I knew exactly what people were going to say to me, and what I would probably try to convince myself of; that I should be grateful that I had these five years with him. No, I was sick and tired of trying my best to put a positive spin on my whole entire life, and I knew the awesome importance that thought had on circumstance, yet what was happening was that I was dying right alongside Guy and I needed a miracle of the highest order.

August 18, 1999

"Robert," Marianne's frantic voice called out to me over the telephone. "Thank God you're home. It's time for you to be over here. You have to come right now. I can't understand anything that your dad is saying. Some of it is French and I think some is Creole." "I'll be there in fifteen minutes Mom." "Hurry, Robert," she said gravely before hanging up.

The hospice care nurses were expert at interpreting physical signs in dying patients and the signals that those signs represent in terms of estimating time of death. Guy was now inside of seventy-two hours to live. Marianne was feeding him teaspoons full of liquid morphine upon instruction from the hospice nurse while I paced from the kitchen to the hallway and back to the bedroom where Guy was lying down with his head propped up on a pillow.

"Can you go in and see if you can make any sense of what he's saying, Robert?" Marianne asked . "Yeah Mom, I will." I noticed as I moved into the room to lie down beside Guy that his eyes were shut very tightly like Marianne said they had been for some time now. She said not to worry about that because it was normal, and that one's sense of hearing is the last to leave, so he could hear what I had to say perfectly. I held my soul's mate closely in my arms, propping his head up until it rested on my shoulder, and listened carefully to what he was trying to say in a tone just barely above a whisper. "My son, we are together in two separate worlds." "Forever, Papa," I answered. Then he grinned and greeted Mama Francine in French. "I wish you didn't have to go, Papa," I cried, my tears splashing his temple and cheek. "Ah, but Robaire, c'est la vie." I pulled him even closer until I could smell his breath, his skin, his hair, and his essence enough so that I would never forget it. "Mama and I are going to be fine. I don't want you to suffer for another minute so it's, it's," and I stuttered at this point, fighting through a choking throat, "it's uh, it's okay for you to go now, Papa." No it wasn't. I was wrecked. Ruined. My entire life was spent being careful with my feelings, never giving away enough to be hurt, and simultaneously picking up on everyone else's feelings around me like a sponge, even when I didn't want to. It was like radar. He's angry, better not go near him now; she's upset, watch yourself around her; they're happy, I guess it's okay to approach them. I never put myself first and let other people react to me, but now I had to forget all pride, fear, humility, or anything at all and just say what I felt. "I love you more that anything in the world Papa and I'm just going to miss you so much—too much. I don't know what I'm going to do without you. I am so proud of you. I'm so proud that you're my father." Guy squeezed my hand in his tightly. "You're my compass, Papa, and I'm going to be lost without you, so lost." Again he said, "We're to-gether in two separate worlds." Then he whispered softly and squeezed my hand again tightly, never opening his eyes, saying, "Robaire, my son, you are my hero." I cried because he made me feel so good when he said that to me. He made me know I belonged, but he was leaving. His breathing suddenly sounded horrible. It was what the hospice nurse called 'The death rattle,' meaning his lungs were filling up with fluid so

it sounded like he was breathing under water. This was the end. The final physical sign, and Marianne and I knew it. She climbed into bed and spooned her lover closely enough to conform to his body like they were one, while I knelt on one knee beside the bed holding onto his hand with my own. If death had any way of being desirable whatso-ever, this was it because Guy was surrounded with love from the two people who loved him most. His little girl, his Anne-Marie, his darling was with him as a lover, clinging to him physically and emotionally while his son, the philosophical stone, who adored him, grasped his hand tightly. I began to sing 'Do-do, Ti-ti' to him out of the blue, not knowing what else to say or do, but realizing as I was singing it how incredibly ironic and appropriate it really was. Death has its similarities to birth and I was singing the Haitian lullaby that we had performed together so many times, comforting him like a baby.

His breaths were getting farther and farther apart, and breathing for Guy was now so incredibly labored that I prayed for him to release and go even while I was singing. Then he sat upright in a ninety degree angle, really bolting upright actually, and opened his eyes as wide as could possibly be for the first time in over twenty four hours and the last time of his life, and stared directly into my eyes for three seconds, branding me with love and a final glimpse of each other's eyes. Then he returned to his prone position and took his last breath.

"Please don't stay in there Robert," Marianne pleaded with me to leave the room where Guy passed away, knowing that he was about to have his body bagged. One more time she implored, "Robert! Don't stay in there." She was sitting in the front room on the sofa, but I just couldn't join her until I was certain that Guy was being treated with the utmost respect to the end. I was always his bodyguard in a sense any way, looking after him and making certain that he was treated with the dignity he deserved. Marianne knew what she was talking about though, as the image of Guy's face disappearing from my view forever behind a zipper was burned into my memory. I walked outside with the two men who were attending to Guy and watched as they put him into the back end of the hearse. One of the gentlemen saw how anguished I was and walked over to me, saying, "I can assure you we'll treat your father delicately and respectfully." "You do that, sir, because that is one great man in the back of your vehicle," I said. The back doors closed, eliminating my view of Guy. My last view. The last time I would see him in a physical manner. As the car pulled slowly out of the driveway, I walked with it a few steps as the harsh reality began to really sink in that my father, my miracle that came back to Marianne and me, was gone, gone forever. The pendulum had truly swung from joy, even pure euphoria, to sadness. I had reached various levels of gut-wrenching grief over the last few months, but the capacity for despair seemed to be growing and growing, until finally, I drug my body back inside the house, the house with one less person in it, and let go crying like a baby, even screaming out in agony as I crossed the living room floor to Marianne, falling to both knees at her footsteps crying, "It's not fair Mom, it's not fair." She agreed through her tears, "I know it Robert, it isn't at all." I wailed and lost my sense of feel, my sensitivity was tarnished, and I could not feel, it was as if my body had gone numb. I could never prepare for the slow, slow thaw that I was in for.

I got in my car after holding onto Marianne for a while then began to navigate the twenty minute drive home, when suddenly, a big burst of air charged into my nostrils almost as if I had turned on the car fan on high and opened the vents pointing them directly at my face. This gush of air stopped me in my tracks causing me to pull off of the Bothell highway into the McDonald's parking lot because I recognized the smell to be absolutely, positively, Guy's breath being blown right into my face. I turned the car engine off, head spinning when it happened a second time even larger. It was my father's breath and the clean scent of his skin wrapping around me like a blanket. My first reaction was to look for a logical explanation so I cupped both of my hands over my own mouth and breathed into my hands, holding the scent in the palms of my hands, then smelled the air I had exhaled to be certain that it wasn't my own breath that was playing tricks on me. It most certainly was not. Mine was a distinctly different scent leaving me with nothing else to do but sit back, smile and say "Thank you, Papa. I needed that." He was comforting me in whatever means were available to him, and I loved the connection that was made in my car, just hours after Guy had left us. My emotions had instantly changed from despair to serenity with the understanding that we really were together in two separate worlds.

EPILOGUE

"The strong, calm man is always loved and revered. He is like a shade giving tree in a thirsty land, or a sheltering rock in a storm. Who does not love a tranquil heart, a sweet-tempered, balanced life? It does not matter whether it rains or shines, or what changes come to those possessing these blessings, for they are always sweet, serene, and calm. That exquisite poise of character, which we call serenity, is the last lesson of culture; it is the flowering of life, the fruitage of the soul. It is as precious as wisdom, and more to be desired than gold-yea, than even fine gold."

JAMES ALLEN, 'AS A MAN THINKETH'

March 1, 2001

"Are you okay, honey?" I called around the corner to Josette, thinking I heard crying coming from the stairwell. My daughter was sitting beside a photograph of Guy and me taken from the cover of a compact disc, and she was crying sadly saying, "I miss my grandpa, Daddy. Can he come down from heaven so that I can see him again just once?" She was very young when Guy passed away, but she had some uncanny connection to him that was frankly unexplainable, and I tried to console her and tell her about death and spirit and heaven, all very abstract ideas for a four- year old mind to grasp. But I had never seen her quite so shaken and sad, so I had to phone Marianne. "Mom," I said, "Josette is really, really affected by Papa being in heaven, and she has been sitting by his picture in my stairway and crying for a while now." Marianne thought it was just adorable how fond of Guy her little granddaughter was, until she had a thought, and said, "Oh my God, do you realize what today is Robert?" "No Mom, what is it?" "It's your father's birthday today!

Later that summer, while in the middle of writing this manuscript, Josette said to me, "Daddy, can I write a book too?" "Sure honey," I answered as I sat her down in front of the keyboard and told her to begin typing. She didn't know how to type at all so she simply randomly let her fingers punch any keys that they landed on. She was all over the keyboard even hitting the numbers on the calculator way off to the right side. I moved into the family room to relax, when she asked, "Can I print my

book like you do, Daddy?" I got off of the sofa and moved over to the monitor to show her how to print what she had just typed. "First sweet pea, let's save what you typed in your own file." I saved her stuff and called it "Scribble." "Now we can print it out, Josette." The printer purred and rattled a bit then quickly spit out two pages of scribble. I sat back down when Josette came over to me, shoving her pages in my face and asked, "Will you read my book to me, Daddy?" At first I didn't want to, it was scribble after all, but Josette was relentless like only a child can be, saying, "Please Daddy," and I sighed heavily, straightening up and told her, "Honey, it's not readable. The letters don't go together into words." But just before I finished saying this to her, the hairs on my arms began to stand straight up and I got goose bumps all over my skin because of what I was seeing on this page of so-called 'scribble'. I got out a pen and circled what I was seeing, what was freaking me out, until I got to the bottom of the page. What I found was the word "Guy," typed over fifty times, and about another twenty times typed backwards. This was the kind of miracle, the kind of magic that only my papa could pull off and I knew it. I smiled broadly and realized for certain that he was communicating through my precious baby girl whom he had simply adored towards the end of his life. Again I called Marianne and she was astounded when I showed her the actual printout.

A few weeks later, with fall around the corner, Marianne, Josette, and I went to spend the afternoon together at the park, sitting down beside this beautiful fountain and soaking up some of the summer's last drops of sunshine together. Directly upstairs from us was a restaurant, so I asked Josette if she wanted a chocolate milkshake. "Yes please, Daddy." "Would you like one too, Mom?" "No thanks, Robert." When I returned to sit beside Marianne, Josette was playing by the fountain, throwing pennies in and making her secret wishes, when Marianne grabbed me by the wrist and looked freaked out. She said, "Robert, Josette just called me 'Little Girl' while you were up getting her milkshake. Can you believe she would call me the nickname that your father had for me?""Mom, she doesn't know anything about that nickname he had for you. Oh my god, he's at it again." Josette walked over to us and said it to her again, this time I witnessed it, "Hi little girl," she grinned at Marianne as she sidled up the way kids do to receive hugs. Marianne looked at me as if to say, "I told you so." It was her first real dose of what Papa had been up to with me for months now, and she was comforted by his presence.

Being a father is the greatest achievement of my life and I am good at it. Every evening that I put Josette to bed, telling her stories and reading to her, saying our prayers together, is one more evening than I ever had at her age. When I watch her skipping down the hallway to go to bed, I nearly cry every time I see it. It reminds me of my vision that I had at the restaurant in Times Square with Guy, the night before our concert in New Jersey. And I can't help but crack her door open at night to peek inside at her asleep to see the most beautiful vision of her. She goes to sleep happy, sometimes with a grin on her face, because she knows her daddy loves her, and she knows she belongs. Even as a child, she's already got what I only just received as a grown man, that is, peace in her heart. Sometimes I like to compare pictures of her and me at the same age and invariably, she is smiling from ear to ear, with a shimmer in her beautiful, big, hazel eyes. When I look at mine, it is such a stark contrast. I am pensive, frowning even in some of the photos. It serves to remind me that I am doing something wonderful. I have a quiet affinity for those who have struggled, and I mean struggled mightily. We know what pain is, what emotional pain is, and without an intimate knowledge of pain, how can real joy ever be truly understood? People say to me, "You're a survivor," and they expect me to feel complimented. No, I am not a survivor. I am a conqueror, a warrior, a hero who has endured things that most will never face. My daughter knows her father, and she knows things as a small child that I learned as a grown man. This is progress at its purest. A smile comes to my face as I ponder what Guy would say about it all, and then I have the answer… "The generation has improved upon itself and justice has been served."

Maestro and Marianne

Josette and I together at Christmas

ISBN 142518443-X

Made in the USA
Lexington, KY
08 July 2011